STRONGER THAN
SUPERMAN

To Dagmar

ROY KIFT

STRONGER THAN
SUPERMAN

A play for people of all ages from eight years onwards

AMBER LANE PRESS

All rights whatsoever in this play are strictly
reserved and application for performance, etc.,
should be made before rehearsal to:
David Higham Associates Limited
5-8 Lower John Street
Golden Square
London W1

No performance may be given unless a licence has been obtained.

First published in 1981 by
Amber Lane Press Limited
9a Newbridge Road
Ambergate
Derbyshire DE5 2GR

0 906399 26 2

Printed in Great Britain by
Cotswold Press Ltd, Oxford

INTRODUCTION

When, in February 1979, Volker Ludwig, the director of the West Berlin Grips Theater, first suggested to me the idea of a children's play on the theme of the handicapped, I was horrified. For a start, I thought the subject too gruesome for a children's audience; and furthermore the predominant house-style in Grips is comedy and song. The combination of style and subject-matter could only—so I concluded—lead to disaster. I at once put the idea out of my head. But luckily, as it turned out, the concept of the play kept nagging me, and a month later I decided to take up the 'impossible' challenge and give it a try.

Knowing nothing on the subject I was forced to turn first to books, and very soon after to first-hand interviews with social workers, hospital nurses, teachers and, most importantly, the families and children concerned. I soon became acquainted with the medical problems. They are formidable, and can at the moment only be alleviated to a certain extent. What, however, struck me as far worse were the social difficulties faced by handicapped people in a world only too eager to turn its back. In this respect my initial reaction to the idea of the play—horror and rejection—had been a perfect mirror of society as a whole. Faced with a wheelchair person, it is we, the so-called healthy people, who gape in blinkered embarrassment, or turn away in dumb awkwardness, frightened by this living challenge to our world of fitness, beauty and perfection. A 'natural' feeling of sorrow arises in our hearts, but sorrow never helped anyone; indeed, it is only a short step from sorrow to contempt, and we do the handicapped a great disservice by feeling sorry for them.

Only positive action can help to change the situation: action by the handicapped and non-handicapped together. Here we must be aware of the dangers of falling into the 'charity-trap'. For too many people, a pound or two in a charity-box is a convenient way to buy off their bad consciences and have done with the problem. What is more, we must question whether this money is used in the best interests of the handicapped. If it is only used to build swimming pools for the handicapped, or adventure playgrounds for the handicapped, or to provide holiday homes for the handicapped, or improve workshops for the handicapped (to name but a few well-intentioned aims), then I would claim that this only serves to reinforce the ghetto situation of the handicapped. Rather than isolating the handicapped, we should be doing all in our power to integrate them into 'our' world. If we can flatten kerb-stones for motorcars and goods vehicles, we can surely do the same at every street corner for wheelchairs (at the same time doing a service to parents with prams), start thinking about ways of giving them access to buses and underground systems, or even getting into telephone boxes. We could ensure that all new buildings are designed to allow the handicapped full use, and that all renovations to old buildings, including cinemas and theatres, are carried out with the needs of wheelchair people in mind.

Most effective of all, we could start seriously to integrate the handicapped child into the normal school system, and later into the world of work alongside the non-handicapped. For those who assert such ideas to be hopelessly utopian, I can only say that they are at present being practised in Sweden, and pilot projects are being undertaken in West Germany, the results of which have been shown to be of advantage, both academic and social, to the handicapped and the non-handicapped alike. We are not talking about a small percentage of the population. According to the last estimates of the World Health Authority, approximately ten per cent of the world's population is handicapped, i.e. roughly five and a half million people in England, and eight hundred thousand people in London alone. Where are they?

1981 has been designated as the United Nations Year of the Disabled (ugh! horrible word!) Person, and many theatres and groups around the world will be performing this play. All well and good, but it was never written with such a jamboree in mind. Indeed, the play would probably be more effective in changing people's attitudes to the handicapped if it were performed in any year *other* than 1981. The problems facing us are enormous and much needs to be done to bring the handicapped out of the ghetto into a fulfilling life *together with* the rest of us. I can only hope that this play is a small contribution to this process, and look forward to the day when it has made itself redundant.

Finally, I should like to thank all those who helped me in the preparation of the play, who not only showed me all the things that handicapped people are capable of, but who also demonstrated that the label 'handicapped' does not have to trail in its wake connotations of helplessness, hopelessness, ugliness, idiocy or pity. Those who agreed to be interviewed include many families from the South London branch of ASBAH (the Association for Spina Bifida and Hydrocephalus), particularly the Cudd's, the Glazebrook's, the Burr's, Mr and Mrs Terry Denyer, Mr and Mrs Alan Twyford, Wendy Webb, Suzanne and Paula, who kindly allowed me to spend a couple of days with them, the teachers and children of Cotswold School in Streatham, nurses and staff and a social worker from Queen Mary's Hospital in Roehampton, Christopher Masterson, who took me out for a day in Central London, and lastly Bernadette, whom I met in hospital and whose surname I never learnt. Her simple explanation of the operation she had undergone, and its effects, transformed just another piece of play-writing research into a heartfelt commitment.

This play is a comedy. Enjoy it!

Roy Kift

Stronger Than Superman was first produced at the Grips Theater, West Berlin, on 7th March 1980, in a translation by Volker Ludwig, with music by Birger Heymann. It was directed by Wolfgang Kolneder and designed by Mathias Fischer-Dieskau, with the following cast: Dietrich Lehmann, Brigitte Stockmann, Christian Veit, Bernd Vollbrecht, Rüdiger Wandel and Susanne Weihreter.

The first production of the play in English was given on 28th March 1981 at the Jeanetta Cochrane Theatre, London, by the Unicorn Theatre Company (Caryl Jenner Productions) with the cooperation of the Central School of Art and Design. It was directed by Stuart Mungall and designed by Rowena Kenward and Paul Wright, with music by Birger Heymann. The cast was as follows:

PAULA	Bridget Ashburn
MR. MOODY	
CINEMA MANAGER	Haluk Bilginer
MOTHER	Ann Curthoys
CHRIS	Simon Jenkins
KEVIN	Nicky Margolis
MR. WRIGHT	
MR. BARRACLOUGH	Jim Wiggins

Birger Heymann's music for Stronger Than Superman is obtainable from the Grips Theater, Altonaerstrasse 22, 1000 Berlin 21, on terms to be agreed between the composer and the presenting theatre.

STRONGER THAN
SUPERMAN

A play for people of all ages from eight years onwards

CAST

CHRIS . . . . a boy of about ten
PAULA . . . . a girl of about nine
MOTHER
MR. WRIGHT . . . . in his late fifties
KEVIN . . . . a boy of about ten
MR. MOODY
MR. BARRACLOUGH
CINEMA MANAGER

Time: the present
Place: the town in which the play is presented

NOTES

1 It is possible to double the roles of MR. MOODY and the CINEMA MANAGER; and of MR. BARRACLOUGH and MR. WRIGHT.

2 'Spastic' references by Chris or Paula should be played without any implication that spastics are in any way an inferior species of handicap. The distinction between spina bifida and spasticity is there to demonstrate that there are different sorts of handicap, and not different grades.

3 Callipers are used by Kevin in Act Two, Scene One. As these are usually made to measure, it is advisable to contact the local hospital as far in advance as possible (at least two months) to see if they have an old pair which will fit the actor playing Kevin. If not, the callipers will have to be specially made, which also takes a lot of time. The local Spina Bifida or Disabled Association will almost certainly be able to help.

4 The playing of the children should be by adults. This may seem at first to be ridiculous. However, all children, and the majority of adults, accept this convention immediately, as long as the characters are not played as lollipop-sucking, plait-twisting, knock-kneed, freckly, lisping clichés.

ACT ONE

SCENE ONE

Home. Living-cum-dining-room. A bed-sofa. A small table with a telephone at the window. A dining-table with a bench seat behind it, and one chair at one side. CHRISTOPHER, *a boy of about ten, is sitting alone behind the table, wearing a ridiculous woman's hat. On the table in front of him is a homburg hat à la Humphrey Bogart.*

CHRIS: [*in a woman's voice*] Help! Help! Help! [*He switches hats to the homburg.*] Hello viewers, this is your star reporter, Christopher Jacob, speaking from Trafalgar Square where a young lady has been sitting stranded on the top of Nelson's Column for the last four hours! [*woman's hat*] Help! [*homburg*] That's her screaming now! [*hats*] Help! [*hats*] Just a minute ago the fire-brigade arrived, led by my old friend, Willy Waterman! Hello Willy! [*He takes a plastic fireman's helmet from the bench and puts it on : in a deep voice*] Hello Chris. Hello viewers. [*hats*] Willy talks like that because he's always working in smoke. Now Willy, you're an expert fireman, what can you do to help this person? [*hats*] Nothing. [*hats*] Nothing? [*hats*] Nothing! There is no ladder in the whole world as long as Nelson's Column! [*hats*] Are you worried, Willy? [*hats*] Worried? Of course we're worried! If she hits the ground from up there, she'll look like a lump of raspberry jam! [WILLY *laughs. He stops.*] Sorry! [*hats*] Can't anybody help? [*hats*] Nobody wants to, nobody cares. Everyone stares and nobody cares! [*hats*] But wait, Willy! [*He takes a cassette recorder from the bench, puts it on the table and switches it on.*] What is that? [*Superman theme music begins.*] Flying in on the horizon! Is it a helicopter? Is it a jet? Is it a rocket, is it a bird, is it a man? No! Diving through the clouds and the rain and the snow and the sun, like a streak of lightning with his blue cape streaming behind him, yes, yes, it's Superman! [WILLY'*s hat and the homburg are thrown in the air for joy.* CHRIS *swoops in as Superman.*] Don't worry, Lois, I'm coming! Snatch! [*He cradles her in his arms.*] What do you think of my muscles, Lois? [LOIS] Oh Superman, I think you're wunnderful! [SUPERMAN] So do I, Lois! Cos I can do anything! Anything in this world. And I don't need help from nobody!

> [*Sound of the front door opening off.* CHRIS *switches off the tape.*]

Mum?... Mum, is that you?

> [*His younger sister* PAULA *enters in a wheelchair.*]

Where've you been so long? Mum's been ever so worried about you.

PAULA: You know them houses they're building round the back? They're for old people.

> [*She wheels round continuously.*]

CHRIS: Old people! Ugh! Nobody said we were being moved next to old people!

PAULA: What's wrong with old people?

CHRIS: They should be put somewhere else!

PAULA: Like handicapped, I suppose!

> [*She is furious. She starts to wheel off.*]

CHRIS: Careful! If you knock any more paint off the furniture, Mum'll go bananas!

PAULA: Well, I hope when you're old, you're put somewhere else!

CHRIS: It's just they can't play or anything... Like football!

PAULA: Granddad always used to play with us!

CHRIS: Granddad used to live with us!

PAULA: There you are then! Don't be so nasty about old people! Granddad was an old people and —

CHRIS: Person, not people!

PAULA: Right, he was a person! He wasn't just old. [*She stands up in the wheelchair.*] Like you, you're a person. You're not just handicapped.

[*She sits on the sofa.*]

CHRIS: It's all right for you. Next term you'll be going to a new school round here. My school's miles away.

PAULA: The bus'll still come and get you.

CHRIS: What happens when I get home though? Who can I play with? Nobody from my school lives round here!

PAULA: Give us a chance! We've only been here two days.

CHRIS: I don't know anybody!

PAULA: None of us knows anybody! That's why I've been exploring.

CHRIS: Do you know how long you've been out?

PAULA: Let me see . . . Fifty years? [*She laughs.*]

CHRIS: Over an hour! Mum's out looking for you in the car!

PAULA: A whole hour! Has my hair gone grey?

CHRIS: Just to get some sausages. [PAULA *gives a gasp of horror.*] You haven't forgotten them, have you? What we going to have for dinner now?

[*Sound of front door.*]

PAULA: Haaaaaa! Mum!

CHRIS: Hide!

PAULA: Where?

CHRIS: Behind the sofa. Get behind the sofa! Quick!

MUM: [*off*] Paula! Christopher!

CHRIS: Yeah? [*to* PAULA] Get your legs in!

[MUM *comes in.*]

MUM: Is she back yet?

CHRIS: Who?

MUM: Which of your twenty-seven sisters do you think I mean? Paula, of course!

CHRIS: I don't think so.

MUM: You don't think so, do you?

CHRIS: No.

MUM: Who brought your wheelchair back in here then? Father Christmas? Paula, come out from behind that sofa! [*nothing*] Paula, can you hear me? [*nothing*] Paula, if I have to come round behind that sofa to get you out, your bottom's going to be so sore you won't be able to sit down for a week!

[PAULA *crawls out from behind the sofa.*]
Where've you been?

PAULA: Out!

MUM: I know you've been out! Stand up when I'm talking to you! Now where?

PAULA: Just . . . [*She shrugs feebly.*] . . . exploring.

MUM: Do you know what the time is?

PAULA: Can't tell the time.

MUM: It's ten past six! A whole hour I've been waiting for you! I've been frantic, I have! Driving round the streets looking for you. With that ring-road so near, and us new in the area, I didn't know anybody I could ask to look after Christopher!

CHRIS: I was all right!

MUM: What would have happened if there'd been a fire?

CHRIS: Willy would have saved me!

MUM: Willy!

PAULA: His friend Willy.

MUM: His friend Willy doesn't exist!

CHRIS: Nor did the fire!

MUM: Well one day it might!

CHRIS: So might my friend Willy!

MUM: Don't talk nonsense! The point is —

CHRIS: Or Superman!

MUM: Chris! The point is —

PAULA: Or Batman!

MUM: Paula! The point is —

KIDS: Or Spiderman!

MUM: Children! The point is —

KIDS: Yes?

MUM: Now I've forgotten what the point is.

CHRIS: The point is we've got enough to do worrying about *real* things . . .

PAULA: Let alone worrying about things that don't exist!

CHRIS: Anyway, if there had been a fire, I'd have been stuck here and burnt to a cinder because you forgot to put me back in my wheelchair! [MUM *groans.*] It's all right, Mum. We forgive you, don't we Paula?

PAULA: [*not catching on.*] Yeah.

CHRIS: Because we all forget things sometimes, don't we?

PAULA: [*catching on.*] Yeah!

CHRIS: So why don't you stop worrying about it, and get me back in my wheelchair!

MUM: Come on then, shift yourself!
   [*She bends. He puts his arms round her neck. She lifts and heaves him off the chair into the wheelchair.*]
   You weigh a ton, you do! Much more lifting and my back'll be ruined!

CHRIS: Then you can have a wheelchair too.

PAULA: If she's having one, I want one!

MUM: Why don't we have one big one for the three of us?

CHRIS: A family wheelchair!

PAULA: With wings and a jet engine!

CHRIS: A Spaceship Enterprise Family Wheelchair!

PAULA: And all of us can fly to the Moon and discover gold and live happily ever after!

ALL: Hooray!

CHRIS: But what are we really going to do? Now we haven't got Granddad anymore?

MUM: We'll manage.

CHRIS: But what if we don't? You wouldn't leave me shut up in a hospital, would you?

MUM: Chris, I'd do anything rather than have that happen.

PAULA: What! Would you put me in a home?

MUM: Never! I love you both and I'm keeping you both.

KIDS: Yes, but how?
MUM: How?
KIDS: How?

Song: HOW HOW HOW?

How can we get by?
None of us are Superman,
None of us can fly.
But the three of us together
Don't seem to be enough
To deal with all our problems
Without a lot of, out a lot of,
Without a lot of fuss.

We're just a single family
With no daddy any more,
Just a single, single family,
One mum, two kids, what's more
All of us are handicapped
Because we've all got more to do,
But we want to stay together,
Yes, we want to stay together,
Forever, together, wouldn't you?
Together, forever, wouldn't you?

[*Repeat second verse, humming as the family lay the table: mugs, knives, forks, plates. Pick up text again with :*]

We want to stay together,
Yes, we want to stay together,
Forever, together, wouldn't you?
Together, forever, wouldn't you?

MUM: [*Coming from kitchen*] Paula, where did you put the sausages?
PAULA: What?

MUM: The sausages I asked you to get.
PAULA: Forgot.
MUM: Oh Paula, honestly!
CHRIS: [*imitating*] Oh Mum, honestly!
PAULA: We all forget things sometimes, don't we?
CHRIS: Yeah!
PAULA: And it don't matter anyway, cos I said I went exploring.
         And guess what I discovered? Just around the corner?
CHRIS: An Easter Egg?
PAULA: A fish and chip shop.
MUM: What are you waiting for then?
PAULA: What?
MUM: Get some fish and chips!
PAULA: [*Makes to go, then changes her mind.*] No!
MUM: No?
PAULA: [*brightly*] Why don't we all go?
ALL: Yeah!
PAULA: [*exiting with* MUM] And I want three large cod, two
         portions of chips and four gherkins. And vinegar and
         tomato ketchup and salad cream . . .
                  [*They exit.*]
CHRIS: And all I'll get is one fish finger and half a dozen chips!

SCENE TWO

Home. PAULA *is hopping up and down from the table to the
sofa, counting as she touches at each end.*

PAULA: Twenty-five . . . twenty-six . . . twenty-seven . . .
                  [CHRIS *comes in in his wheelchair.*]
CHRIS: Where's Mum?
PAULA: Shopping. Twenty-eight.
CHRIS: Can I play?
PAULA: Hopping in a wheelchair!

CHRIS: I don't want to hop in a wheelchair!

PAULA: Well then!

CHRIS: I wanna play something else.

PAULA: Thirty! [*She collapses on the sofa and looks at her watch.*] And it's a new record speed! Exactly one minute!

CHRIS: And that's a new record toy watch!

PAULA: Don't matter, I counted! Each time was two seconds, and I did thirty. Thirty times two is sixty, and sixty seconds . . .

CHRIS: Makes an hour.
[*He begins rolling up and down from the rollator which is standing in the room, to the table and back.*]

PAULA: Minute, 'nana!

CHRIS: Hour, apple!

PAULA: Day, orange!

CHRIS: Week, plum!

PAULA: Year, pomegranate!

CHRIS: One hundred years!
[*He blows a farting noise.*]

PAULA: What's that?

CHRIS: Raspberry! Who cares how quick you were?

PAULA: Just 'cos you're so slow! If you had to hop, you'd take a century!

CHRIS: Like the Sentry at Buckingham Palace?

PAULA: [*Throws a cushion at him.*] You don't half crack some terrible jokes!

CHRIS: Right, what we going to play?

PAULA: I know! 'Doctors and Nurses' and I'll be the doctor.

CHRIS: You can't be the doctor! Only boys are doctors. You're the nurse!

PAULA: Some girls are doctors, so I want to be the doctor.

CHRIS: Look, girls are nurses. You're a girl, so you're the nurse.

PAULA: All right then, people in wheelchairs are patients. You're in a wheelchair, so you're the patient!

CHRIS: That's not fair!

PAULA: It's just as fair as what you said.

CHRIS: I always have to be the patient!

PAULA: And I always have to be the nurse!

> [CHRIS *rolls furiously to the door.* PAULA *sulks on the couch.*]

CHRIS: All right, you be the doctor.

PAULA: [*almost simultaneously*] And you be the doctor!

BOTH: Right!

CHRIS: Ha! No, that won't work.

PAULA: Got it!

CHRIS: What?

PAULA: [*going over to the rollator*] I'll be the patient, you be the nurse.

> [*She climbs on the cross-bar of the rollator.*]

CHRIS: Me, a nurse?

PAULA: Male nurse! [*She slips off the cross-bar and falls awkwardly to the ground, groaning*] Oooooooooh!

CHRIS: What's the matter, Paula?

PAULA: I've got a greenstick fracture of the left leg, just above the shin-bone!

CHRIS: What!

PAULA: A greenstick fracture of the left leg, just above the shin-bone, I heard it on the telly!

CHRIS: [*scathing*] You're not supposed to know that, you're the patient!

PAULA: All right then, I've just been to see the doctor, and he told me.

CHRIS: Shows how much you know about doctors! Doctors go: "What appears to be the problem?"

PAULA: Appears to be! It *is* the problem! [*She sticks her leg in the air.*] See! My leg!

> [*He feels it.*]

CHRIS: Ah-ha — oh-ho — a-hum! [*He writes in an imaginary notebook.*]

PAULA: [*Sits up.*] It's a greenstick fracture of the left leg, just above the shin-bone, isn't it?

CHRIS: Take this note to the hospital, the doctor'll deal with it there.

PAULA: Why don't you tell me? It's my leg, not yours!

CHRIS: [*breaking the game*] Oh look Paula, you've got to have a note!

PAULA: All right, I'll have a note. But you've got to tell me as well!

[*She runs out of the room.*]

CHRIS: Hey, where you going?

[PAULA *re-appears with an envelope and drops it on his lap.*]

PAULA: Get a note! Here!

CHRIS: Get this patient to the hospital immediately!

PAULA: Eh! Why?

CHRIS: This is an emergency, we haven't got time to talk about it!

[*He lays* PAULA *across his wheelchair. They both make ambulance siren noises as he wheels her to the table.*]

Here, doctor, I'll put her on the operation table.

[PAULA *rolls off the wheelchair onto the table.*]

PAULA: Doctor? We haven't got a doctor!

CHRIS: We have now! Male Nurse Chris calling Superman! Come in, Superman!

[*Chanting 'Superman' music he does a wheely, i.e. spins round in his wheelchair on two wheels, then rolls to the table.*]

PAULA: Help, Superman! Help!

CHRIS: [*as Superman*] Have no fear, Lois! Here I am! Examination! [*He feels her leg up and down.*] I'm afraid I'll have to amputate!

PAULA: What?

CHRIS: Cut the leg off!

PAULA: Not until you tell me what's wrong with me!

CHRIS: You're too small to understand.

PAULA: How am I going to understand anything if you don't tell me!

CHRIS: [*Pushes her down onto the table.*] Gas! Pssssssssss!
　　　[*He detaches one of the arm-rests from his wheel-chair and turning it upside down uses it as a saw.*]
　　　Operation!
　　　[*He saws off* PAULA's *leg.*]
　　　Operation completed!
　　　[*He puts back his arm-rest.* PAULA *sits up.*]

PAULA: Patient dead! [*She flops back melodramatically.* CHRIS *rolls away and picks up the 'note' that is tucked in his chair.*] And if ever I have a doctor who acts like Superman, I'm going to ask for another! How about your friend Willy?

CHRIS: Here! This is a letter. Guess who from?

PAULA: Who?

CHRIS: The Council! Bet it's from the new Social Worker.
　　　[*He starts to try to open it.*]

PAULA: What you doing? That's for Mum.

CHRIS: "It's my legs, not hers!"

PAULA: Go on then.

CHRIS: It's not been stuck down very well. See. We'll stick it back again with glue . . . What did I say! Social Services.

PAULA: What's it say?

CHRIS: "Dear Mrs Jacob . . ."

PAULA: That's Mum.

CHRIS: Of course it's Mum! "Thank you for your letter informing us of your new address. As the new Area Super . . ."

PAULA: Superman!

CHRIS: Super-*visor*! Supervisor in charge of Christopher, I should like to take the oppor . . . oppor . . .

PAULA: Operation.

CHRIS: How can a Social Worker take an operation? Honestly!

PAULA: Opportunity?

CHRIS: That's what I was going to say! ". . . opportunity of bringing up once again the possibility of Christopher being — ”

[*He stops in horror.*]

PAULA: What's the matter? What's it say? [*She takes the letter.*] “. . . of Christopher being sent away to a Home” ! What ! The rotten — ! “I know you have already talked about this with the previous social worker . . . bla bla bla bla” Who wrote this? “D.J. Barraclough. Area Supervisor.”

CHRIS: Give me that letter! [*He snatches the letter.*] Mum's never said a word about me being sent away to a Home. I don't want to be packed away in a Home what's miles and miles away from here. I mean, school's far enough but at least I can come home in the afternoon. Like everyone else! [*He tears the letter up and crumples it into a ball, then throws it on the floor.*] Mr Barraclough!

PAULA: I'll stick it in the dustbin!

SCENE THREE

Home. CHRIS *is sitting alone at the table, hitting it with a length of rope.* PAULA *comes in with a bundle of dirty washing and throws it in the middle of the room.*

PAULA: What you doing that for?

CHRIS: Nothing.

[PAULA *goes out.* CHRIS *continues hitting the table.* PAULA *returns with more dirty washing.*]

PAULA: What do you think you're up to?

CHRIS: I'm beating up that Mr Barraclough!

PAULA: I don't think that's funny.

CHRIS: It's not meant to be funny.

PAULA: Come on, Chris. Let's play something, eh?

CHRIS: [*grumpy*] What, Doctors and Nurses?

PAULA: No hang on, I know! [*She runs out of the room, then*

*returns with a Roman helmet and whip. She puts the
helmet on* CHRIS's *head and gives him the whip.*] Now
you're the Emperor and I'm the washerwoman, and I've
got to wash the Emperor's dirty underpants . . . [*She
hangs a sheet round her neck.*] . . . and shirts, and socks,
and everything. [*She kneels before* CHRIS.] And I have to
be really humble. "Humble, humble, humble!"

CHRIS: Wait a minute! I've got a better idea! I'm Julius Caesar,
and I've got to get to Rome as quick as I can to throw
Barraclough to the lions!

PAULA: Oh yeah!

CHRIS: And you're my washerwoman slave, and you've got to
pull my chariot!

> [PAULA *hangs the rope around the handles of the
> wheelchair and gets into her 'harness'. She begins
> to pull the chariot.*]

Faster, slave, faster!

> [*She pulls him round the room a couple of times.
> He improvises like mad as Julius Caesar.*]

PAULA: Mercy! Mercy!

> [*The wheelchair goes a bit too fast.*]

CHRIS: Not so fast, not so fast! Mind the washing!

> [*She trips and stumbles among the washing.*]

PAULA: Mercy! Mercy!

CHRIS: How dare you leave the Imperial Roman Washing on the
Palace floor!

PAULA: Mercy on a poor working mother, Julius!

CHRIS: What did you call me!

PAULA: Julius Caesar.

CHRIS: *Mr* Caesar to you! Julius only to my friends! And on top
of that, I'm the Emperor Caesar! [*He cracks his whip.*]
Attention, slave!

PAULA: Ow!

> [*She runs and hides under the table.*]

CHRIS: [*rolling after her*] You, slave, are accused of driving the
Imperial Roman Chariot slower than the permitted five

miles per hour because you were drunk!

[*He cracks his whip.*]

PAULA: I don't drink beer!

CHRIS: Drunk on milk!

[*He cracks his whip.*]

PAULA: That's impossible!

CHRIS: Don't answer back! You are also accused of dirtying the Imperial washing by chucking it all over the Imperial Palace floor. How do you plead?

PAULA: On my hands and knees!

CHRIS: Don't be so cheeky! Guilty or not guilty!

[PAULA *comes from under the table.*]

PAULA: It was already dirty.

CHRIS: You're supposed to make it cleaner not dirtier!

PAULA: You clean it then; you made it dirty in the first place!

[*She throws a couple of sheets at him.*]

CHRIS: I am the Emperor, I can do what I want!

PAULA: You sound like one of our stupid teachers!

CHRIS: Silence in Court! I'm the judge!

PAULA: I thought you were the Emperor; how can you be the judge?

CHRIS: The Emperor makes the judges.

PAULA: Can't I be the judge?

CHRIS: You're the slave. [*She goes into a huff and sits on the sofa. He picks up the phone.*] Members of the Jury, how do you find this woman? Guilty!

PAULA: What?

CHRIS: Guilty, I'm the Jury too! I sentence you to life imprisonment in the galleys, rowing the Imperial boat from the Palace to the Imperial fish and chip shop and back! And in your holidays, of which you shall have none because you've got to look after me, pushing my chariot to the sweetshop and back. Have you anything to say?

PAULA: Not on your Imperial Nelly!

[*She puts her tongue out.*]

CHRIS: What! Are the slaves revolting?

PAULA: You bet we are !

> [*She throws a sheet over his head and spins him round in his wheelchair.* CHRIS *flails with his whip.*]

CHRIS: Guards ! Bodyguards ! Help ! Murder !

> [MUM *comes in with a basket of washing.* CHRIS *hits her with the whip.*]

MUM: Ow ! Careful, Christopher !

CHRIS: Sorry, Mum.

MUM: All right, but be more careful next time, will you. [*He nods. She gives him a kiss.*] Paula, I want a word with you. [*She opens a bed sheet. There is a large yellow stain on it.*] What's this ?

PAULA: [*attempting a joke*] Orange Squash ?

CHRIS: [*putting his oar in*] Sunfresh Orange Drink.

> [PAULA *looks daggers at him.*]

MUM: You haven't wet the bed for years, and now you do it two days running ! What sort of a life is it for me if I've got to change your sheets every day ? Eh ? Well ? What have you got to say ? [PAULA *shrugs guiltily.*] At your age too !

PAULA: Chris does it, and he's older than me !

MUM: Chris can't help it.

PAULA: Oh yes he can ! That's what he had that operation for ! That's what he had that bag for !

MUM: It's not Chris's fault if it sometimes breaks.

PAULA: Just because he's handicapped, he gets away with everything !

MUM: Paula, you know that isn't true !

PAULA: You treat him like a big baby !

CHRIS: Who !

PAULA: You ! And when he gets too much for you, I have to look after him all the time ! I'm fed up of being your slave !

> [*She storms out of the room.*]

MUM: Paula ! [*She sighs and starts gathering up the washing.*] I don't know what's got into you two. These last two days you've been treating me like an enemy. What is it ?

[*The front door bell rings.*]
Paula, answer the door, will you!

CHRIS: [*ill-tempered*] *I* can answer it too!

[*He wheels off.* MUM *continues folding the washing.*]

WRIGHT: [*off*] Is your mother in?

CHRIS: [*off*] Yes.

WRIGHT: [*off*] I'm selling flags to help the old people.

MUM: [*to herself*] More money for charity!

[CHRIS *wheels in.*]

CHRIS: There's a man at the door.

MUM: Ask him in then.

CHRIS: He can't.

MUM: Of course he can! [*She calls off.*] Come in, will you.

[*She continues folding the washing.* MR WRIGHT *enters in a wheelchair. He is a lively man in his late fifties.*]

Which one is it this time?

WRIGHT: Help the Aged.

[MUM *turns and starts with surprise at the wheelchair.*]

MUM: Oh! [*half amused*] You should be collecting for the handicapped!

WRIGHT: This? [*He slaps his legs.*] Old age! And I used to be an athlete.

CHRIS: Really?

WRIGHT: Really.

MUM: What about something to help mothers, that's what I say.

[*She opens her purse.*]

WRIGHT: That's what families are for.

MUM: Families, did you say? My husband's no longer here, my youngest is upstairs sulking, he's in a wheelchair, I've got to get some shopping in for lunch, I'm trying to get the washing ready for the launderette because my washing-machine's broken yet again, and this afternoon I've got to

	take him off for an appointment at the hospital!
WRIGHT:	Hospital! I hate hospitals. I've had three operations.

    [MUM *drops a coin into his tin and takes a flag, then goes back to her washing.*]

CHRIS: I've had fifteen.

WRIGHT: At your age!

CHRIS: Fifteen!

MUM: Getting on for two a year till now.

WRIGHT: And all because of your handicap?

CHRIS: Right.

WRIGHT: Were you in an accident?

CHRIS: No. I've been like this since I was born.

WRIGHT: You mean you've never been able to walk.

CHRIS: No. [*He taps his legs with his whip.*] Never had the message.

WRIGHT: Message? What message? I don't understand.

    [CHRIS *holds up his whip.*]

CHRIS: What's that?

WRIGHT: A whip.

CHRIS: OK. Let's pretend that's me.

WRIGHT: You're a bit thin!

CHRIS: I am, aren't I! Here... [*Holding the whip at arm's length he indicates the top of the handle.*] ... is my head. And here... [*While he speaks he winds the coloured strands of the whip around the handle.*] ... are the nerves. And the head sends its messages to the legs through the nerves... [*He gives a whistling sound and indicates the message going round the nerves to the other end of the whip.*] ... to the legs here! [*He places the whip handle against his chest.*] The head says... [*He speaks into the 'head' of the whip.*] "Legs, walk!" [*He looks over the whip head to his legs. No reaction. He tries again.*] "Hello legs! Can you hear me? I said 'Wa-alk!'"

WRIGHT: [*not understanding*] But they don't move.

CHRIS: Right. Because somewhere in my backbone... [*He takes *the strands of the whip and breaks them in the middle. He holds up the broken strands for a second and then drops them on the floor.*] . . . the connection's broken.

WRIGHT: Oh, I understand. That's why your legs have never had the message!

CHRIS: Right.

WRIGHT: And that's what they call spastic.

CHRIS: No, that's what they call spina bifida.

WRIGHT: Spina bifida, I thought you were spastic.

CHRIS: [*not in the least contemptuous*] No! Spastic's something entirely different. Like dialling the wrong number. Look. [*Same action with the whip against his body.*] The head says: 'Legs walk!' [*His left arm shoots into the air.*]

WRIGHT: But your arm moved.

CHRIS: That's what I mean. The head gives a very clear order to the body and the muscles get it all mixed up.

WRIGHT: He talks like a doctor!

CHRIS: No, better! Doctors never explain anything!

MUM: They do to me, Chris.

CHRIS: Not to me.

WRIGHT: Or to me.

[MR WRIGHT *is sitting with his back to the door.* PAULA *appears furiously at the door with a pillow.*]

PAULA: [*to* MUM] Anyway, I don't care if he does go away to a Home! So there!

[*She thumps* MR WRIGHT *on the head with the pillow.*]

WRIGHT: Ow!

PAULA: Oh!

MUM: Paula!

PAULA: [*accusingly to* CHRIS] What are you doing over there? [*to* WRIGHT] Who are you?

MUM: Paula, say sorry to the gentleman immediately!

PAULA: Sorry, I thought you were Chris.

WRIGHT: Do I look so young?

PAULA: No, just the opposite.

MUM: Paula!

WRIGHT: It's all right. At least she's honest.

PAULA: [*to* WRIGHT] *You* can stay here if you want.

WRIGHT: Instead of who?

PAULA: Instead of Chris. When he gets sent away to a Home.
[*Shocked silence for a moment.*]

MUM: Whoever said anything about Chris getting sent away to a Home?

CHRIS: What if the new social worker says I've got to?

MUM: I shall listen. I shall consider. And *I* shall have the final say!

PAULA: And you won't tell us until after you've done it.

MUM: [*amazed and hurt*] Oh! Now! . . .

CHRIS: Well?

MUM: Look, the last social worker suggested I should think the matter over —

CHRIS: You never told us that.

PAULA: Why didn't you tell us?

MUM: Because I didn't want you worrying unnecessarily!
[PAULA *and* CHRIS *come out with a jumble of questions and accusations over which* MUM *tries to impose some order.*]

PAULA:⎱ What if the new one says I've got to?
CHRIS:⎰ Yeah it was all right so long as Granddad was here . . .
You still could have told us . . .
Now there's only you, and you don't care! . . . [*etc., etc.*]

MUM: Children please! [*Silence at last.*] I have not the slightest intention of putting Christopher in a Home . . . Right?
[*Pause. The children nod.* MR WRIGHT *clears his throat.*]
Oh! Er . . . I'm dreadfully sorry, Mr . . . er . . .

WRIGHT: Wright.

MUM: [*thrown*] Pardon?

WRIGHT: Mr Wright. That's my name. I live just around the corner. [*to the* KIDS] Right?
[*The* KIDS *smile.*]

MUM: Well, as I said —
WRIGHT: Don't say anything! Where's that shopping-list?
MUM: Pardon?
WRIGHT: I think your mother's going deaf! [*The* KIDS *laugh.*]
There's more to helping people than collecting money.
Have you got a shopping bag?
MUM: Very well then!
[*She goes out happily.*]
WRIGHT: [*to* CHRIS] You wanna come?
PAULA: Him, shopping!
WRIGHT: Why not?
PAULA: He's never been in a supermarket in his life!
WRIGHT: Well now's a good time to start!
[PAULA *nods and goes off.*]

Song: YOU DON'T GIVE ME THE CHANCE

BOTH: There's many many things that I can do
And many many things I can't
But what I really hate is when
You don't give me the chance.
Have a heart now, use your head,
It don't take much to realise
If you'd only let me try
You might get a big surprise!

Many people treat us
Like zombies from another world,
You should hear the things they say
It makes you want to weep . . .
With laughter!

WRIGHT: 'Look at him! Poor thing can't walk!
Don't 'spect he can even talk!

CHRIS: 'When a person's in a chair
It's obvious he's not all there!'

WRIGHT: 'Can't do nothing on his own
Best thing's put him in a home !'

CHRIS: 'Like a baby with a teat
Smile and wave and give him a sweet !'

[MUM *comes back with her shopping bag and hangs it on* MR WRIGHT*'s wheelchair. She gives* CHRIS *a purse.*]

BOTH: There's many many things that I can do
And many many things I can't
But what I really hate is when
You don't give me the chance.
Have a heart now, use your head,
It don't take much to realise
If you'd only let me try
You might get a big surprise !

[*They wheel off.*]

SCENE FOUR

Most of the stage is taken up by a patch of private building land. This is fenced off from the narrow public footpath with a wire fence and warning notices. However, one part of the fence has been broken away, enabling children to get onto the land and play. Here we see KEVIN, *who is trying without much success to do tricks with a football.* MR MOODY, *a security guard, arrives. He is chewing a sweet.*

MOODY: Here, you !
KEVIN: What ?
MOODY: Off ! This is a demolition site, not a playground.
KEVIN: Where am I supposed to play then ? On the ring-road ?
MOODY: Less of the lip ! Off ! [KEVIN *makes to go.*] I'm only saying for your own safety. Dangerous, see !

KEVIN: What they demolishing?
MOODY: Nothing. That's finished.
KEVIN: What's dangerous then?
MOODY: They're building.
KEVIN: Where?
MOODY: They're going to be building. Off!
KEVIN: It's been like this for months!
MOODY: And very soon men are going to be building here.
KEVIN: Can't I play on it till they — ?
MOODY: No, you can't! I said it's dangerous!
KEVIN: What's the danger?
MOODY: It's private property! Off!
KEVIN: [*Goes towards the fence, then stops.*] What they going to build here?
MOODY: Car park. Off!
KEVIN: Why not a playground?
MOODY: Look, working adults need somewhere to park their cars!
KEVIN: Look, working children need somewhere to play after school!
MOODY: All right clever, come here... Come here!... If you're so clever, come here! [KEVIN *comes over.*] Take a look round. What do you see?
KEVIN: Nothing.
MOODY: A great patch of nothing. And that is valuable!
KEVIN: Nothing is valuable?
MOODY: [*stamping on the ground*] It's called land. Might look like nothing to you, but land is money. And the people who own this land want to get their money back quick!
KEVIN: What for?
MOODY: To buy *more* land, of course.
KEVIN: What for?
MOODY: To make more *money*, of course!
KEVIN: What for?
MOODY: To buy more *land*, of course!

KEVIN: What for?

MOODY: To make *more* money, of course! And they ain't going to get it from building playgrounds, are they? Ain't going to get it from your pocket-money! Now, off! And if I see you once more back on here, I'm calling the police. Understood?

> [KEVIN *is about to go through the fence when the security guard pulls him back. He has seen* CHRIS *in his wheelchair.*]

KEVIN: Here! What you doing?

> [MOODY *nudges* KEVIN.]

MOODY: [*secretively*] There!

KEVIN: What?

> [CHRIS *enters in his wheelchair.* KEVIN *gapes.*]

MOODY: [*whispering*] Poor kid! Spastic!

KEVIN: Yeah?

MOODY: Bit... [*He makes a sign to indicate that* CHRIS *is mental.*] ... You know!

> [KEVIN *gapes.* CHRIS *becomes aware that he is being stared at. He glances over.* KEVIN *and* MOODY *look away.*]

MOODY: [*loudly*] Yeah, well, er, you heard what I said! Private!

> [CHRIS *looks away.* MOODY *and* KEVIN *stare back at him.*]

Sad, really. Should be put away.

KEVIN: Killed?

MOODY: Wouldn't go that far. I mean, they're no use to no-one really, are they? I mean, never be able to work or nothing.

> [CHRIS *looks up again.* MOODY *raises his hand in the air and gives a big smile, nods and waves. He nudges* KEVIN *to do the same. The two of them wave, nod and smile like glazed puppets.* MOODY *walks over to* CHRIS *awkwardly and drops a couple of sweets through the fence onto his lap.* CHRIS

stares at them for a moment, then wheels off.]

MOODY: Phew ! [*to* KEVIN] Thank your lucky stars you're not a bit
 . . . [*He grunts like a mental defective, and begins to nod
 like a spastic.*] Ugh, ugh, ugh ! [*in a deep nutty voice*]
 Give us an ice-cream, Mister ! [*He pretends to take the
 cornet.*] Ta !
 [*He wobbles with the cornet before his mouth,
 then suddenly plops it in his eye. They both laugh.*]
 Well, you got to, haven't yer ? What's life without a larf ?
 [*suddenly threatening*] And remember . . . Police !
 [*He watches* KEVIN *go through the fence to the
 other side, then goes.* KEVIN *does a few grunts to
 himself and imitates the ice-cream joke. He laughs
 to himself.* PAULA *comes on. She looks round for*
 CHRIS, *then walks through the broken fence onto
 the private land.*]

KEVIN: Hey !
PAULA: Yeah ?
KEVIN: You can't go on there.
PAULA: Why not ?
KEVIN: Private property.
PAULA: Just exploring.
KEVIN: There's a bloke over there. Throw you off.
 [PAULA *looks to where* KEVIN *has pointed.*]
PAULA: Can't see no-one.
 [KEVIN *comes through the fence.*]
 Is that a football ?
KEVIN: Yeah.
PAULA: Give us a kick.
KEVIN: Don't play with girls.
PAULA: Who do you play with then ?
KEVIN: On me own.
PAULA: One-man football ?
KEVIN: Used to have a lot of friends round here.
PAULA: What happened ?

KEVIN: Got re-housed. Demolition. For the ring-road.

PAULA: Give us a kick then?

KEVIN: No.

PAULA: Please yourself.
    [She starts to go.]

KEVIN: Where you going?

PAULA: Home to my brother.

KEVIN: You got a brother?

PAULA: Yeah.

KEVIN: How old?

PAULA: 'bout your age.

KEVIN: Play football?

PAULA: School team.

KEVIN: What position?

PAULA: Attack.

KEVIN: *[really interested]* You live round here?

PAULA: Just moved.

KEVIN: I'm a goalie. D'you think he'll play with me?

PAULA: If you want.

KEVIN: Course I want! Will you tell him?

PAULA: If you let me have a kick of your ball.
    [KEVIN kicks the ball over. PAULA flicks it up onto her knee, flicks it from side to side a few times and passes it back to him. He gapes.]
He's a great swimmer too, my brother. Going in for a medal.

KEVIN: Racing?

PAULA: Life-saving.

KEVIN: Wanna bit of chewing gum? *[PAULA holds out her hand. He throws her a piece. She catches it.]* My name's Kevin.

PAULA: My name's Paula.

KEVIN: *[furtively excited]* Guess what I just seen!

PAULA: What?

KEVIN: Spastic.

PAULA: Where?

KEVIN: In a wheelchair. [*He starts grunting and shaking.*] Ugh, ugh, ugh . . . Oi'm a spastic. Ugh . . . Give us an ice-cream!

[*Same joke. He roars with laughter. She does not.*]

PAULA: I don't think that's funny at all.

KEVIN: You got to laugh though, haven't yer?

PAULA: No.

KEVIN: They don't understand anyway. They're mental!

PAULA: What do you know about it?

KEVIN: Don't get so ratty! Hey! Here he comes again!

[*He turns away from* CHRIS, *who has re-entered.* PAULA *makes a quick motion with her hand to* CHRIS *to remain where he is.*]

PAULA: How d'you know he's spastic?

KEVIN: Use your eyes!

PAULA: How d'you know he's mental?

KEVIN: They all are.

PAULA: Let's go and ask him.

KEVIN: Eh?

PAULA: Why not?

KEVIN: Well . . .

PAULA: Come on, why not?

KEVIN: I won't know what to say to him.

PAULA: He won't bite you.

KEVIN: I know he won't bite me!

PAULA: What's the problem then?

KEVIN: I ain't never spoken to one before.

PAULA: I thought you knew all about them! [*She calls to* CHRIS.] Here!

CHRIS: [*uncertain*] Yeah?

PAULA: [*She goes over.*] It's all right. This is Kevin. I've just met him. [*to* KEVIN] Say hello then.

KEVIN: Mm . . . [*He gulps.*] . . . Hello then.

CHRIS: Hello.

KEVIN: [*to* PAULA] What's his name?
PAULA: Ask him.
KEVIN: What's your mm . . . what's your . . . what's your . . . what's your name?
CHRIS: Have you got a stammer?
KEVIN: No. Why?
CHRIS: I was just wondering why you were stammering.
KEVIN: [*to* PAULA] Do you know him?
PAULA: His name's Chris.
CHRIS: [*to* PAULA] What about him?
KEVIN: Kevin. [*to* PAULA] Why don't he speak to *me*?
PAULA: Cos you don't speak to him.
KEVIN: Whose side are you on?
PAULA: My brother's!
KEVIN: Is he your brother!
PAULA: Yeah, of course he is.

> [KEVIN *stares at* CHRIS *for a moment, embarrassed and bewildered. Then the penny drops.*]

KEVIN: Oooooooooh! You never told me you had *two* brothers!
PAULA: I haven't.
KEVIN: Eh? [*He beckons to her to tell her something in private. In a low voice.*] I want to ask you something.
PAULA: What about?

> [KEVIN *nods in the direction of* CHRIS *and jabs with his thumb madly.*]

KEVIN: Him.
PAULA: Well ask *him* then.
KEVIN: Can't.
PAULA: Why not?
KEVIN: [*Mouthing; no voice.*] Well! You know!
CHRIS: Has he lost his voice or something?
KEVIN: No!
CHRIS: I thought for a minute you'd gone dumb.
KEVIN: Nothing wrong with my voice, you really a spastic?
CHRIS: No.

PAULA:　What did I say?

　　　　　[KEVIN *stares at* CHRIS, *thoroughly confused; then after a pause the penny drops again.*]

KEVIN:　Oooooooooh! I get it! You been having me on, you can't walk when you can! Nice one! Good trick! [*He goes to the fence.*] Here, come on in! [CHRIS *wheels through the fence.*] Fantastic! [*He thumps* CHRIS *playfully on the shoulder.*] What did you say your name was?

CHRIS:　Chris.

KEVIN:　Kevin. Come on then! Out of that chair, I want a go!

CHRIS:　Look, I can't get out. I can only walk with crutches.

KEVIN:　[*over* CHRIS *to* PAULA] You mean he really is spastic?

PAULA: }
CHRIS: } [*simply*] No.

CHRIS:　What I was born with is called spina bifida. My legs are lame.

　　　　　[KEVIN *looks confused for moment.*]

KEVIN:　Of course! What am I talking about? [*He taps his skull.*] You're not stupid, are you! Like, I mean, spastics . . .

　　　　　[*He goes into his spastic routine but* CHRIS *cuts him off very quickly.*]

CHRIS:　And spastics aren't stupid either! They're as bright as I am, they've just got problems talking!

PAULA:　Right! The only people who are stupid are the stupid people like you, who make stupid jokes about spastics!

　　　　　[KEVIN *stands there embarrassed for a moment.*]

KEVIN:　[*over* CHRIS *to* PAULA] I thought you said he could swim.

CHRIS:　[*to* PAULA] Why don't he talk to me? Why does he always have to say everything to you?

PAULA:　Oh! Was he talking to me?

CHRIS:　He asked you a question.

PAULA:　He asked me a question?

CHRIS:　He asked you a question.

PAULA:　What question?

CHRIS:　I dunno. He didn't ask *me* the question.

KEVIN:　[*pointing*] *I* asked *her* the question! About *you*!

CHRIS: [*pointing*] Oh! *He* asked *you* the question! About *me*!

PAULA: Ooh! [*pointing*] *He* asked *me* the question! About *you*! [*to* KEVIN] What *was* the question?

KEVIN: Whether he could swim.

CHRIS: Will *you* tell *him*, the answer to his question is yes.

KEVIN: All right, I get it, sorry, apologise! Right?

CHRIS: Will *you* tell *him*, his apology's accepted?

KEVIN: [*jabbing his own chest*] Talk to me!

CHRIS: I can swim a quarter of a mile.

KEVIN: Without legs!

CHRIS: Well, I do take 'em with me! I don't just cut 'em off and leave 'em on the bank!

KEVIN: I can't even swim *with* legs!

CHRIS: Aaaaaah!

KEVIN: What?

CHRIS: What a terrible handicap!
[*They all laugh.* PAULA *takes the ball from* KEVIN *and throws it to* CHRIS.]

PAULA: Here you are, Chris.
[*He heads it.*]

KEVIN: Pretty good! Bet you can't get one past me, though.
[*He lines up against the fence as goal and throws the ball to* CHRIS. CHRIS *heads it back.* KEVIN *pretends to save it but lets it in.*]
Great goal! Fantastic!

PAULA: Eh! You didn't even try to save it!

KEVIN: I did!

CHRIS: You think I can't score past you.

KEVIN: You just did!

CHRIS: I mean properly!

PAULA: If you kick the ball as stupidly as you play in goal, no wonder no-one'll play with you!

KEVIN: I can kick the ball hard!

CHRIS: How hard?

KEVIN: This hard!
[*He boots the ball as hard as he can. It flies away*

         across the building site. He runs after it, then stops
         and turns.]
     Oh no! There's that bloke coming back again! He's
picked up the ball.

PAULA: Ask him for it then.

KEVIN: He said he'd call the Police!

CHRIS: Against us?

KEVIN: Not you! He thinks you're simple. Here he comes!

CHRIS: Hide! Hide!

         [PAULA *and* KEVIN *run off and hide.* CHRIS *stays*
         where he is. KEVIN *pokes his head out of hiding.*]

KEVIN: Hurry up! He's coming!

         [PAULA *runs to fetch* CHRIS.]

CHRIS: I know! Get in! Paula!

         [*She runs back and hides.* MOODY *appears with the*
         ball.]

MOODY: All right, where are you, you little monkey? Come on!
     [*He sees* CHRIS *and speaks to him as if he's very simple.*]
     Have you... seen... a little boy? [CHRIS *nods.*] Where?
     [CHRIS *taps his chest.*] No! I mean... with a football!

CHRIS: Oh!

         [*He points at* MOODY.]

MOODY: No! Me not a little boy! You... a little boy!

CHRIS: Oh!

MOODY: I'm looking for a *naughty* little boy.

CHRIS: Eh?

MOODY: Naughty! You know... [CHRIS *shakes his head.* KEVIN
and PAULA *are now peeping out.*] Naughty! Like they go
... [*He puts his tongue out.*] Or... [*He puts his thumb on
his nose and waves.* CHRIS *looks bewildered.*] Or... [*He
jumps up and down, screaming like a baby. He picks his
nose and eats it.*[

CHRIS: Eh?

MOODY: Or... [*He shoves his bottom in the air and gives a loud
farting noise*] ... which is very naughty and deserves a
smack.

CHRIS: Eh?

MOODY: A big smack! [*He holds out his hand.*] Smack! [CHRIS *smacks it hard.*] Ouch! Not me! A little boy . . . [CHRIS *points to himself.*] . . . With a football! [CHRIS *holds his hand out for the football.*] Yeah, that's right! [*He gives* CHRIS *the football.*] Have you seen one?

CHRIS: Eh?

MOODY: Seen one!

CHRIS: Eh?

MOODY: Have you . . . [*He points to* CHRIS.] . . . you . . .

CHRIS: Yeah?

MOODY: Seen a little boy with a football?

CHRIS: Yeah!

MOODY: Where?

CHRIS: Here!

[CHRIS *holds up the ball and points to himself.*]

MOODY: Noooooooooooooo!

CHRIS: Yeeeeaaaaaaaaah!

MOODY: Oh forget it! Some people! Cor, I don't know! Dear me!

[*He goes off muttering to himself furiously.* KEVIN *and* PAULA *come out of hiding.* CHRIS *waves to them to hide behind his wheelchair, then calls after* MOODY.]

CHRIS: Hey you!

MOODY: [*off*] Yeah?

CHRIS: Anyone who acts like you needs his head looking at! Thanks for the football! Run!

[*They run off, pushing* CHRIS. MOODY *runs on.*]

KEVIN: [*Puts his head round the corner.*] Terrific, eh!

END OF ACT ONE

ACT TWO

SCENE ONE

Home. PAULA *is lying on the sofa.* CHRIS *is sitting in his wheelchair. Both are reading comics. The door-bell rings.*

CHRIS: ⎫
PAULA: ⎬ I'll go!

    [CHRIS *is quicker. He wheels off. After a few moments he comes back.*]

CHRIS: It's Kevin.

    [KEVIN *enters uncertainly. He is holding a bar of chocolate. He is very uncertain and doesn't quite know how to begin. The other two stay relaxed and friendly.*]

KEVIN: Mm . . . hello.

PAULA: Hello.

    [*Pause.*]

KEVIN: Well . . .

CHRIS: ⎫
PAULA: ⎬ Well?

    [*Pause.*]

KEVIN: [*suddenly aware of the chocolate in his hand*] Oh! Yeah! My Mum said to give you this chocolate.

CHRIS: Thank you.

    [PAULA *snatches if from* CHRIS.]

PAULA: Great!

KEVIN: Hey! That ain't for you, it's for Chris!

PAULA: He's not allowed to eat chocolate.

KEVIN: How come?

PAULA: If he eats too much he'll get fat.

KEVIN: Eh?

CHRIS: I've got to watch what I eat, cos I don't get so much exercise sitting in a wheelchair.

KEVIN: Oh! . . . Yeah. [*Pause.*] Is this your room then?

CHRIS: No, this is the living-room.

PAULA: Where we play.

KEVIN: Oh!

[*He gives a short laugh. He looks around and his eye catches something by the table. He is slowly engrossed, and bends to look under the table. The other two bend to look under the table.* KEVIN *starts and straightens up.*]

Have you only got one chair?

PAULA: We don't need any more.

KEVIN: Eh?

PAULA: I'll show you. [*She sits on the bench behind the table.*] I sit with Mum here. Or here. And Chris sits here or here.

[*She indicates the sides of the table where there are no chairs.*]

KEVIN: Oh yeah . . . [*He laughs uncertainly.*] . . . How come? [CHRIS *wheels to the table.*] Oh, I get it! You've always got your chair with you! Great, fantastic! I mean . . . er . . . Do you have to sit the whole day long in that chair?

CHRIS: No. From time to time I walk with crutches.

PAULA: [*enthusiastic*] You wanna see?

KEVIN: Mm . . . Yeah.

[PAULA *is already out of the room without waiting for his answer. She comes back with two crutches. They are like walking sticks with four feet. She places them in the middle of the room.*]

They ain't crutches!

PAULA: What else are they, stupid!

CHRIS: They're made like that so's I don't fall over.

KEVIN: Oh.

[KEVIN *takes hold of the crutches and walks down the room with them as if they were walking sticks.*]

CHRIS: Not like that! I can't walk like that!

[KEVIN *stops, then proceeds to move across the room with huge two-legged hops.*]

Not like that either! For a start, my legs are straight.

[KEVIN *now tries to move with straight legs, supporting his whole weight with his arms.*[

KEVIN: Cor . . . you got to be real strong for this. Need a bit of muscle-power!

CHRIS: When I first had them I was always falling over.

PAULA: He had to learn with another thing!

[*She runs off to fetch it.*]

CHRIS: I should really practise every day.

[PAULA *comes back with the rollator.*]

PAULA: Here! See! My favourite toy.

KEVIN: Let me have a go! [*He proceeds down the room with stiff legs, finding it much easier. He stops.*] Hang on! You said straight legs. Yours are bent!

CHRIS: Cos I'm sitting down, aren't I! See, I've got callipers on.

[PAULA *pushes up* CHRIS's *trousers to reveal a bit of the callipers.*]

PAULA: They're called callipers.

CHRIS: And when I want to walk, there's a catch here at the knee, and the callipers go straight.

PAULA: Tell you what Chris, we've got an old pair out the back! Shall I get 'em?

[*Without waiting for an answer she runs off. She returns with a huge pair of callipers joined at the waist.* KEVIN *looks shocked.*]

CHRIS: That's exactly the same as what I'm wearing.

PAULA: Do you want to try them too?

KEVIN: Mmm . . . er . . . shall I?

PAULA: Why not! [*She puts the callipers on the sofa and leads* KEVIN *over.*] You're not afraid, are you?

KEVIN: Me?

PAULA: Lie down then.

KEVIN: What for?

CHRIS: You can't put 'em on unless you lie down.
[PAULA *pushes him down onto the sofa.*]
PAULA: OK . . . Take your trousers off!
KEVIN: [*Sits up.*] Eh!
PAULA: Trousers off!
KEVIN: Don't want to.
CHRIS: You've got to!
PAULA: Chris does.
CHRIS: I do! Trousers off!
BOTH: Trousers off! Trousers off! Trousers off!
KEVIN: I can put 'em on top of my trousers!
CHRIS: Callipers go under trousers not on top of them.
KEVIN: What if your Mum comes in?
PAULA: She'll laugh herself stupid because of your skinny legs!
KEVIN: They are not skinny!
PAULA: Bet they are!
KEVIN: Bet they aren't!
PAULA: Show then!
[KEVIN *jumps on the sofa. He rolls up his trouser legs and stands there defiantly with arms folded.*]
KEVIN: See!
PAULA: [*Falls to her knees.*] Oh my hero! Knobberly-knees!
[KEVIN *hastily rolls his trousers down.*]
KEVIN: Can I have a go in your wheelchair?
CHRIS: Do you really want to?
KEVIN: Yeah!
CHRIS: OK.
KEVIN: Great!
[*He runs to the wheelchair.*]
CHRIS: But first you've got to have the callipers.
[KEVIN *hesitates a moment.*]
KEVIN: Where's your Mum?
[PAULA *runs outside, then returns.*]
PAULA: [*in a loud whisper*] In Chris's room. Making the bed!
KEVIN: Keep watch!

[PAULA *nods. She stays by the door. During the next section she peeps at* KEVIN *when she gets the chance. When* KEVIN *sees her he tells her not to look.*]

KEVIN: Here Chris, give us a hand, will you?

[KEVIN *has slipped his shoes off, and then his trousers, and is now sitting on the bed.*]

CHRIS: [*beside the sofa in his wheelchair*] First of all, stick your leg in them... See. Like great football socks...! Now you have to do up all these straps... Tight as possible so's it won't slip.

[*This must be improvised as it depends on the type of calliper used. In the meantime* PAULA *has crawled under the table to watch from there. When the callipers are on* CHRIS *wheels away.*]

KEVIN: The knees won't bend!

CHRIS: They're not supposed to! They're to stop your legs collapsing.

KEVIN: Yeah, but yours are bent!

CHRIS: Because I'm sat down. There's a catch at the side, by the knee, and when you want the callipers bent, you pull it.

[KEVIN *pulls the catches. He sits on the sofa with bent knees.*]

KEVIN: [*triumphantly*] I got it!

[*He stands up. He goes to walk across the room but falls flat on his face because the callipers lock straight automatically. He sits up.*]

Cor, they rub a bit.

[*He makes them bent again.*]

CHRIS: They do me.

KEVIN: Don't they hurt?

[*With the help of the rollator he gets to his feet.*]

CHRIS: Course not!

KEVIN: Eh! Why?

PAULA: He can't feel a thing!

KEVIN: Eh?

CHRIS: My legs are paralysed. I can't feel anything from my waist downwards.

KEVIN: No kidding!

CHRIS: Pinch my leg.

KEVIN: You sure?

CHRIS: Go on! Hey Paula, do you remember . . . ?

[*He turns and whispers something to* PAULA. *In the meantime* KEVIN *pinches* CHRIS's *leg.* CHRIS *turns back to* KEVIN.]

Come on then. What you waiting for?

KEVIN: I already have . . . ! Eh!

[*He lunges to pinch* CHRIS *again as hard as possible.* PAULA *pulls* CHRIS's *wheelchair out of reach.*]

PAULA: Steady! Else he'll have a bruise!

CHRIS: I once broke my leg playing football.

PAULA: He didn't know he'd done it.

CHRIS: Till Mum saw the bruise.

PAULA: His leg was all bent!

KEVIN: Ugh!

PAULA: [*Points to* KEVIN.] Ugh!

KEVIN: What?

PAULA: Don't you want to put your trousers on?

[KEVIN *cries out. He runs for his trousers and naturally falls flat on his face again. He reaches for his trousers and tries to put them on with straight legs. He finds it impossible and releases the catch at the knees to make them bent.*]

That's cheating!

KEVIN: Take me hours if I had to do it with straight legs.

CHRIS: I have to every morning.

KEVIN: How long's it take you?

CHRIS: Callipers, clothes and washing . . . about an hour. Mum helps, of course.

[KEVIN *sits with his trousers on.*]

KEVIN: Crutches!

> [PAULA *brings him the crutches and places them on
> either side of him with the handles facing his feet.*
> KEVIN *looks at her and makes a sign to indicate
> that she's loony. He turns the crutches round with
> the handles facing him, then grasps them and tries
> to pull himself to his feet.*]

PAULA: ⎱ Wrong!
CHRIS: ⎰

> [KEVIN *changes his hand position and tries again.*]

PAULA: ⎱ Wrong again!
CHRIS: ⎰

> [KEVIN *stares at the crutches, confused, and then
> returns them to the original position where* PAULA
> *had put them, and rolls over onto his stomach.*
> PAULA *makes a loony sign back to him.* KEVIN
> *grasps both crutches and tries to lift himself to his
> feet.*]

CHRIS: Body-building, are we Kevin? [KEVIN *collapses onto his
stomach.*] Hey Kevin, why don't you try getting up, just
with one crutch?

> [KEVIN *grasps one crutch and pushes himself with
> effort to his feet. He then takes the other crutch.*
> CHRIS *and* PAULA *cheer and applaud.* KEVIN *waves
> a crutch in triumph.*]

KEVIN: Done it! [*He goes into a game straight away.*] Here comes
Long John Silver and his old parrot. "Pretty Polly!
Pretty Polly!" Quiet! [*to* PAULA] And you're Jim
Hawkins.

PAULA: [*Joins him with a salute.*] Yes sir!

KEVIN: Ah-ha, me hearties! Is that the Captain's wheelchair I
see, down in the harbour? Please Captain, take pity on
an old sea-dog and let him rest his tired and rusty legs!

CHRIS: Very well, Silver. But you must pay with your crutches.

KEVIN: "Pretty Polly! Pretty Polly!" Quiet!
[*He passes the crutches to* CHRIS, *who stands with* PAULA's *help.*]

PAULA: [*Makes whistling noises to pipe the Captain ashore.*] The Captain's going ashore. Captain, sir!
[*She salutes as* CHRIS *leaves the chair.*]

KEVIN: [*as* KEVIN] At last, the wheelchair!

PAULA: That's not a wheelchair, it's the ship!

KEVIN: [*sitting*] That's what I mean, ship! Hoist the sails!
[PAULA *climbs on the back of the chair.*] Full speed ahead for Africa!
[PAULA *practically falls over* KEVIN *because the wheelchair doesn't move as the brakes are on.*]

CHRIS: Raise the anchor, you land-lubbers! The anchor!
[KEVIN *releases the brakes, and he wheels* PAULA *round the room.*]

PAULA: Long John Silver, sir! [*She points at the table.*] An island!

KEVIN: That's the Isle of Dogs! We want Africa!

PAULA: [*Spies* CHRIS.] Long John Silver!

KEVIN: Yes Jim?

PAULA: [*pointing at* CHRIS] Pirates!

CHRIS: I'm the Captain!

KEVIN: Not any more, you're not! Throw him in the dungeon!
[CHRIS *tries to escape towards the table.*]

CHRIS: Treason!

KEVIN: In the dungeon, I say! How dare you pretend to walk like Long John Silver!

PAULA: [*to* CHRIS] You're arrested.
[*She takes his crutches as he sits on the bench behind the table. She puts the table back in position as if it were a rusty prison door, then runs to fetch the rollator.*]

KEVIN: "Pretty Polly! Pretty Polly!" Quiet! For the last time!
[KEVIN *mimes strangling the parrot and dropping it on the floor.* PAULA *takes the rollator and places*

it over CHRIS's *head with one end on the table and
the other on the back of the bench.*]
What's that supposed to be, Jim Hawkins?

PAULA: The prison, sir!

KEVIN: He'll escape!

PAULA: Not this way, sir!

[*She throws the table cloth over the rollator,
covering* CHRIS *completely, then salutes Long
John Silver.*]
Mission accomplished!

[CHRIS *throws the table cloth off.*]

CHRIS: Give me a chance!

KEVIN: Trying to escape, eh? Death! Death to the Pirates!

[PAULA *throws a crutch to* KEVIN. *He catches it and
they both proceed to machine-gun* CHRIS *to death.*
CHRIS *shoots back wildly. All three die long and
bloody deaths. Pause.* MUM *appears with a bag of
dirty washing.*]

MUM: Hello dead-men! I'm off to the launderette. Oh, you
must be Kevin. Nice of you to come round. [*She picks up
the crutches and places them by* CHRIS.] Be back in ten
minutes.

[*She goes.*]

KEVIN: Is that all it is then . . . your handicap?

CHRIS: What?

KEVIN: Well . . . walking.

CHRIS:⎱ Yes.
PAULA:⎰ No.

KEVIN: Make up your mind.

PAULA: No, it isn't. Can I tell him? [CHRIS *shrugs.*] He's a bit shy
about it, see.

CHRIS: I'm not.

PAULA: You are.

KEVIN: [*very curious*] What is it then?

PAULA: He had an operation, see. Because he was always wetting
himself.

KEVIN: Ugh!

PAULA: And so to stop him doing it, he's got a bag. And all his...
his water...

CHRIS: Goes in there.

PAULA: [*enthusiastically*] Hang on, I'll show you!
[*She runs out.* KEVIN *wheels up to* CHRIS.]

KEVIN: And this bag... goes over your willy?

CHRIS: No. They did an operation near my kidneys, here. [*He
points to* KEVIN's *kidneys.*] Just under your belly-button.
And the water comes out through a hole into the bag.
[PAULA *comes back with the bag.*]

PAULA: See! Just like a plastic balloon! [*She blows it up and
waves it around.*] The water goes in this, and it all fills up.
[*She sticks it in place on her belly.*]

KEVIN: Ugh!

PAULA: What's the matter with you then?

KEVIN: My Mum and Dad say we don't talk about that sort of
thing in our family.

PAULA: Well, in our family we have to.

CHRIS: If you don't talk about it, you can't do nothing about it!

KEVIN: Yeah, but —

PAULA: But what? Cor, you don't mind playing at killing and
death and murder!

KEVIN: That was a game!

PAULA: You don't mind talking about killing, but you go all
funny and stupid when we have to talk about something
real like a little plastic bag! Honestly!
[*She slams the bag onto* KEVIN's *chest where it
sticks. He delicately removes it and looks at it.*]

KEVIN. Do all handicapped people have bags?

CHRIS: [*amused*] No.

PAULA: [*pleased because he asked directly*] Not all of them.

CHRIS: Spina bifida people like me —

PAULA: A lot of *them* do.

CHRIS: But spastics and others probably don't at all.

KEVIN: I thought they was all the same.

CHRIS: What! There's about a hundred —
PAULA: Thousand —
CHRIS: Million —
PAULA: Billion —
CHRIS: Trillion —
PAULA: Different sorts of handicap.
CHRIS: About as many different sorts as there are people.

Song: MANY MANY FOLK

CHRIS: There's many many folk in wheelchairs,
        Many other folk on crutches,
        Many many more are deaf or dumb,
        However, maybe not as much as . . .

PAULA: ⎱ Some who walk funny, or who talk a bit funny,
CHRIS: ⎰ Or who hold a knife and a fork a bit funny,
        Some who limp funny, or who wink funny,
        Or who wave or who nod or who drink a bit funny.

CHRIS: Many of us may look funny
        A few of us may look quite sad,
        But if you'd only get to know us
        You'll find it ain't so bad.
        Some of us have floppy muscles,
        Some of us have jerky arms,
        But if you'd take the time to know us
        You'll find there ain't no harm.

PAULA: ⎱ Just like every big cathedral
CHRIS: ⎰ Has a slightly different steeple,
        We're four hundred thousand million
        Slightly different people
        Like you!
            [*The front door-bell rings.*]
PAULA: Mum!
CHRIS: She forgot the key again!
            [PAULA *runs out.*]

PAULA: [*off*] Yes.

MR B: [*off*] Is your mother in?

PAULA: [*off*] She's down the launderette.

MR B: [*off*] She's expecting me, I believe. Mr Barraclough's the name.

CHRIS: [*horrified*] Hey Kevin. Barraclough!

> [*He hides under the table-cloth.* KEVIN *stays in the wheelchair.*]

PAULA: [*off*] She'll be back in a couple of minutes, why don't you come in?

MR B: [*off*] I wrote to her from the Social Services Department. About your brother.

> [MR. BARRACLOUGH *appears in the doorway with* PAULA. *He is carrying a brief-case. He is a middle-aged bureaucrat, smart and smooth.*]

You do have a handicapped brother, don't you? [*He raises his arms as he sees* KEVIN *in the wheelchair.*] Ah yes! How are you then, Christopher, you're looking very well I must say! Nice and bright!

> [*He tickles* KEVIN *under the chin.*]

KEVIN: Ugh!

> [KEVIN *points to* CHRIS. MR. BARRACLOUGH *turns.*]

MR B: And who's your friend over there under the table-cloth? Nice of you to come and play with him! [CHRIS *comes out from under the cloth.*] There's no need to be frightened of me, I'm the head of the local Social Services Department.

> [*Meanwhile* PAULA *has been making hand signals to* KEVIN *to stay in the chair and play the game out.* KEVIN *makes hand signals back and mouths dialogue.* MR. BARRACLOUGH *turns and catches them in mid-action. They stop immediately.*]

Oh, I'm so sorry! No-one informed me he was deaf and dumb.

KEVIN: Ugh!

CHRIS: He's not.

MR B: Just physically handicapped.

CHRIS: He's not physically handicapped.

MR. B: No?

CHRIS: No! I am!!

> [PAULA *looks daggers at* CHRIS. MR. BARRACLOUGH *turns slowly to look at* KEVIN, *then turns back to* CHRIS.]

MR. B: That sort of joke is not in the least funny, young man! [PAULA *and* KEVIN *begin to snigger.*] Just because you're lucky enough to be normal, like me! [*to* PAULA] I'm not sure you should be laughing either. Though I'm glad to see Christopher's taking it in the right spirit.

CHRIS: My name's Christopher.

MR. B: Too! Christopher one and Christopher two!

> [*He laughs loudly. The* KIDS *don't.*]

PAULA: Have you come about sending him to a Home?

CHRIS: You're not sending me away to a Home!

MR. B: I don't intend sending you anywhere young man. It's *this* Christopher I'm worried about. School, for example.

KEVIN: Eh? My school's just around the corner.

MR. B: It might be just around the corner to you! But I think we really know, when we think just a little bit about it, don't we, that your school is a long long way from your new house here.

PAULA: The bus can still come and get him.

MR. B: The bus has to go around the town picking up all the other handicapped little boys and girls.

KEVIN: So what's the problem?

MR. B: The problem is, Christopher —

CHRIS: Yes?

MR. B: I'm not talking to you! [*to* KEVIN, *patronisingly*] The problem is that your house would be one of the first stops.

KEVIN: And?

MR. B: The bus would have to get here very, very early.

CHRIS: How early?

MR. B: [*to* CHRIS] Please! [*to* KEVIN] About an hour before school starts. If not more! And you know how long it

             takes you to get dressed and ready *before* that. It's not
             only you we've got to think about —

CHRIS: It's me.

MR. B: [*almost as a reflex*] It's you. No, it's not you! Please don't
             interrupt! [*to* KEVIN] We have to think about your dear
             mother. And what time she has to get up to get you ready.

CHRIS: If the only problem's the bus . . .

MR. B: [*with a weary sigh*] Yes?

CHRIS: Why don't you have more busses?

                    [MR. BARRACLOUGH *leaves* KEVIN *and bears down*
                    on CHRIS.]

MR. B: Oh! you're the expert, are you?
                    [*He twists* CHRIS's *ear.*]

CHRIS: Yes.

MR. B: You know more about it than me, I suppose?

CHRIS: Might do.

MR. B: You can speak up for yourself, I suppose?

CHRIS: I'm learning to.

MR. B: But who's going to speak up for Christopher, if not me?

CHRIS: Me!

MR. B: I mean this Christopher! [*He returns to* KEVIN.] After all,
             he's not like you, is he?

CHRIS: That's true!

MR. B: He's not cheeky like you! He's a little bit retiring.

CHRIS: Eh?

MR. B: Shy. Like all handicapped. [*to* KEVIN] We've scarcely
             heard a squeak out of you since I arrived.

KEVIN: You haven't given me the chance, that's why!

MR. B: Well er . . . come along then, Christopher . . .

CHRIS: Yes?

MR. B: [*ignoring the interruption. to* KEVIN] What do you want to
             know, eh?

KEVIN: Mm . . .

MR. B: [*to* CHRIS] There you are, you see!

KEVIN: Is that all you've come about? School?

MR. B: A-hem! [*blustering*] In some respects, yes.

PAULA: Or have you come to stick him in a Home?

MR B: [*furious*] Really!

KEVIN: What have you come about then?

PAULA:
CHRIS: } What have you come about then?

MR B: Well er . . .

KIDS: Well er?

MR B: [*Turns* KEVIN's *wheelchair away from* CHRIS *and* PAULA.] I'm here to try to deal with Christopher's . . . total needs! For example, his callipers. So, Christopher —

PAULA: Do you know how long he had to wait for his new callipers?

CHRIS: Three months!

MR B: I think we've heard quite enough from you! [*to* KEVIN] So, Christopher —

[MOTHER *enters unseen in the doorway.*]

PAULA: And what about a new washing-machine?

CHRIS: Mum has to go down the launderette twice a week because of all the extra washing!

MR B: [*over his shoulder*] This has nothing to do with you! [*He points at* KEVIN.] Christopher's not complaining!

KEVIN: I don't know anything about it, that's why!

MR B: You see! He's perfectly satisfied!

KEVIN: I didn't say that!

MR B: But that's what you meant!

KEVIN: No!

CHRIS: And what about a shower in the bathroom?

PAULA: So's he can wash himself without Mum having to lift him all the while!

MR B: [*exasperated*] Mum, mum, mum!! Where is 'Mum' anyway?

[MUM *enters.*]

MUM: Here! What's the problem?

[MR. BARRACLOUGH *spins round. He tries to regain his composure.*]

MR B: I was merely trying to make it clear . . . to the children . . .

that the Council is doing everything in its power to help your Christopher . . . and indeed all the handicapped.

MUM: [*deeply ironic*] Wonderful! I'm delighted to hear it! Maybe you could do away with a few kerb-stones so he can get his wheelchair across the road without having to ask people all the time. Then you could think about redesigning the busses and the underground to save us the expense of taxis.

MR B: Now, now, excuse me! We're building schools especially for the handicapped, houses especially for the handicapped, workshops especially for the handicapped when they've finished school, and as you well know . . . Homes specially for the handicapped.

CHRIS: Yeah, yeah! So the handicapped are always stuck away amongst themselves!

MUM: We're living here though! And we intend to stay here. For a start you can do something about the front steps!

MR B: [*Blows his top.*] We can't rebuild the whole world, can we! We can't perform miracles! [*He pulls up, and attempts to relieve the situation with a joke.*] You'll be asking me next to make him stand up and walk!

ALL: What?

[*They turn to* KEVIN.]

MR B: Stand up and walk! Ugh!

[KEVIN *stands up and walks towards the shocked* MR. BARRACLOUGH.]

[*BLACKOUT*]

SCENE TWO

*A cinema foyer. Poster of the current film: 'Superman'.
At the box-office stands the* MANAGER *in a suit. Before him
stand* KEVIN *and* PAULA, *with* CHRIS *in his wheelchair.*

KEVIN: We only want to see the film!
MANAGER: Please don't misunderstand me —
PAULA: But you don't want us in the cinema!
MANAGER: On the contrary —
CHRIS: You don't want *me* in the cinema!
MANAGER: [*protesting*] No!
PAULA: So we *can* come in the cinema!
    [*They head for the auditorium entrance.*]
MANAGER: No! I mean, yes! I mean... [*He chases them and blocks
    the entrance to the auditorium with a red cord.*] ... Stop!
CHRIS: Is it because of me, or isn't it?
MANAGER: [*leading* KEVIN *to one side*] Now this has nothing to do
    with me personally, because *I* don't decide these things
    . . .
    [KEVIN *breaks away.*]
KEVIN: *He* asked you the question! Why don't you answer *him*!
MANAGER: I am!
PAULA: You're not. You were talking to him!
MANAGER: There's no need to take that attitude.
KEVIN: All we want to do is see the film!
MANAGER: And we must be phoned in advance if you're going to
    bring someone in a wheelchair!
KEVIN: I think I'm going crazy!
MANAGER: All we require is half an hour's notice to remove certain
    seats in the cinema to make way for the wheelchairs.
KEVIN: It takes you half-an-hour to move one seat!
MANAGER: I'm sorry, the film has just started. Come back tomorrow
    and you'll be very welcome.

[PAULA *starts for the exit with* CHRIS.]

KEVIN: We had to walk here because they wouldn't let him on the bus!

MANAGER: I'm sorry, that has nothing to do with me!

[*The* MANAGER *attends to other matters at the box-office.*]

PAULA: Come on, Kevin.

[KEVIN *gets an idea. He runs to the others, and then over to the auditorium entrance waving to* CHRIS *and* PAULA *to join him. He begins a chant which they take up.*]

KEVIN: He hates handicapped! He hates handicapped! He hates handicapped . . . !

[*The* MANAGER *rushes between them and the door.*]

MANAGER: All right, all right, quiet! You can come in, right? [*He signals them to the box-office. They cheer.*] On condition that he leaves his wheelchair in the foyer.

KEVIN: What? He can sit next to us in the gangway!

MANAGER: I'm afraid not. Fire regulations. Nothing to do with me! If there's a fire in this cinema —

KEVIN: [*pointing to* CHRIS] It's his wheelchair, tell him!

MANAGER: [*to* CHRIS] A fire, yes? And your wheelchair's blocking the gangway, the other people in the cinema aren't going to be able to get out, are they?

KEVIN: Hang on!

MANAGER: Yes?

KEVIN: If there's a fire in there, and his wheelchair's out here, how does he get out?

PAULA: You don't worry about him burning to death!

MANAGER: On the contrary! That's exactly why we have wheelchair places.

KEVIN: Huh!

PAULA: Just prejudice!

[MR. WRIGHT *wheels out of the auditorium to complain. He finds his way blocked by the cord.*]

MANAGER: Oh no it isn't, young lady ! You see that gentleman there.

PAULA: It's Mr. Wright.

CHRIS: He won't let us in, Mr. Wright.

[*The* MANAGER *frees the exit.*]

MANAGER: Dear me ! [*to* MR. WRIGHT] Would you mind if I asked you a couple of questions, sir ?

WRIGHT: You're the Manager, I take it.

MANAGER: That's correct. Did you or did you not telephone the box-office before you came this afternoon ?

WRIGHT: I did.

MANAGER: And as a result, did we or did we not let you in ?

WRIGHT: You did.

MANAGER: [*to the children*] There's your answer then !

WRIGHT: You made me come here a quarter of an hour before everyone else, so nobody would be offended by a wheelchair person in the audience !

MANAGER: I hardly think that was the reason.

WRIGHT: No ? Then why was I packed right away to one side. I'm so far from the screen I can hardly see it !

MANAGER: The reason is, sir, that we have as yet no places specially designated for the handicapped, and that we have to remove certain seats beforehand to make way for the wheelchairs.

KEVIN: Why ?

MANAGER: Why !

PAULA: Yeah, why haven't you got any places for the handicapped ?

MANAGER: Because we don't have that many handicapped people wanting to visit us, what's why !

KEVIN: It ain't surprising, if you make it so difficult !

MANAGER: [*shouting*] Let's just keep calm, shall we ! [*He brings himself under control.*] I can assure you . . . that seats for the handicapped . . . are one of our highest priorities. But what can we do if we haven't got the money ?

WRIGHT: You had the money to buy that land out there for a car-park !

KIDS: What ! Him !

MANAGER: Now that er . . . I don't know where you er . . . I'm er . . . I'm er . . . Look, that has absolutely nothing to do with me!

PAULA: Nothing to do with you! That's what you're always saying!

KEVIN: It's you who's stopping us from going in! Come on, forget it!

[*He makes for the entrance.*]

MANAGER: One more step and I shall be forced to take certain measures!

KEVIN: Eh? What you talking about?

MANAGER: I shall be forced to summon the Police.

WRIGHT: Now, now, now . . .

KEVIN: Ah, stuff it! Come on, let's get in there!

[*The* MANAGER *grabs* KEVIN *and manhandles him towards the office. The others protest.* KEVIN *kicks the* MANAGER, *who yells and releases* KEVIN. KEVIN *runs out of the cinema pursued by the* MANAGER.]

MANAGER: Stop that boy! Stop that boy!

[*Off. The sound of car brakes screeching and a huge crash.* PAULA *runs to the exit door.*]

PAULA: Kevin!

[*BLACKOUT.*]

SCENE THREE

The empty plot of land. PAULA *enters, pushing the wheelchair. She glances perfunctorily through the fence and enters the private land.* CHRIS *comes on behind her, using his crutches.*

PAULA: I don't know what you're so scared about!

CHRIS: It's all right for you, he never saw you. But if he sees *me*, after the trick I played on him . . .

PAULA: He can only shout at you, can't he?

CHRIS: [*half serious, half playfully*] Yeah! [*He shouts.*] And I don't like being shouted at!

PAULA: [*shouting*] You can always shout back at him!

CHRIS: [*shouting*] Me! Shout! I don't know how to! Anyway, it's Kevin who has to — [*He turns: no-one.*] Where's Kevin?

PAULA: Kevin!

[*They retrace their steps.*]

BOTH: Kevin!

CHRIS: He was here behind me!

[*Unnoticed by them,* KEVIN *wheels on in a wheelchair from the private side of the land.*]

BOTH: Kevin! Kevin! Where are you?

KEVIN: Here behind you!

CHRIS: What you doing there?

KEVIN: Came through another hole in the fence back there. [*He tries to push himself up a bit in order to see a bit further.*] I been looking out for that bloke! I can't see a thing down here. It's all right for you, you can walk!

CHRIS: So will you soon.

PAULA: Just be patient!

CHRIS: In six weeks you'll be out of that wheelchair and walking again.

KEVIN: Yeah, and I'm fed up already. Can't do anything. Can't get on a bus, can't ride a bike. Can't even go to bed without being helped.

PAULA: [*Pats him on the head.*] Ah, you poor thing!

KEVIN: And I hate people smiling at me and patting me like I'm a pet dog!

CHRIS: Here Kevin, I know what we'll do for you!

KEVIN: What?

CHRIS: We'll buy up this empty bit of land and turn it into a world for wheelchair people!

KEVIN: Here?

CHRIS: Yeah! And call it Wheel-land!

PAULA: Yeah!

> [*She jumps into* CHRIS's *wheelchair.*]

CHRIS: Now you two are time-travellers travelling into the future! [*He does a count-down.* KEVIN *and* PAUL *travel noisily into the future.*] Stop! Stop, oh time-travellers! Welcome to Wheel-land!

PAULA: [*spinning round*] But it's wonderful!

CHRIS: And I... [*He climbs on the back of* KEVIN's *wheelchair.*] ... am your official travel guide. The first thing visitors to Wheel-land notice is that our country is completely flat!

KEVIN: No steps! Ramps and underpasses everywhere!

CHRIS: So's you can wheel wherever you want!

PAULA: Even the streets are on wheels!

> [*Both wheelchairs are wheeling round the land.*]

CHRIS: And when you go shopping, all the doors slide automatically open —

KEVIN: Whiisssssshhhhh!

CHRIS: When you wheel towards them! And welcome to the Supermarket!

KEVIN: Where all the shelves are low enough to reach!

CHRIS: [*Mimes serving himself.*] Chocolate!

KEVIN: And chewing-gum!

CHRIS: And liquorice allsorts!

KEVIN: And lollipops!

CHRIS: And there's no problem wheeling past the cash-desk.

> [*They wheel between* CHRIS's *crutches.* PAULA *wheels to meet them as the cashier. She peep-peeps on her cash register and holds out her hand.*]

PAULA: Money please! [*They pay up.*] Thank you.

> [CHRIS *gets off* KEVIN's *wheelchair and takes his crutches once more.*]

And now Kevin, we've got enough money to go to the pictures.

CHRIS: And in the cinema there aren't any seats at all!

KEVIN: Eh?

CHRIS: Cos everybody rolls up in their own seats!

PAULA: Yeah, yeah, and you know what we learn in school in Wheel-land?

BOYS: What?

PAULA: The Four R's!

KEVIN: Four R's?

PAULA: Reading, writing, rolling and arithmetic!

CHRIS: Yeah, yeah, and opposite Wheel-land are our deadly enemies.

KEVIN: Old People!

CHRIS: No! Leg-people! Know why?

KEVIN: Cos they think we're stupid!

CHRIS: Worse than that. Cos they build their world with something really criminal: that should be punished with death! Steps!

PAULA: }
KEVIN: } Steps!

CHRIS: And stairs, and kerb-stones.

PAULA: Everywhere!

KEVIN: In front of shops.

CHRIS: And telephone boxes.

PAULA: And all the houses.

CHRIS: Death to the leg-people!

ALL: Death to the leg-people!
       [*They all shoot madly.*]

KEVIN: [*craftily*] Wait a minute, Paula! Look! [*He points to* CHRIS.] A leg-person!

CHRIS: No, I'm on crutches!

PAULA: Death to the leg-people!
       [PAULA *and* KEVIN *shoot at* CHRIS.]

CHRIS: Pack it in! Give me my chair back!
       [PAULA *and* KEVIN *wheel through the fence and off, shouting 'death to the leg-people'.* CHRIS *chases them as fast as he can go, calling after them.*]
       I want my chair back! Give me my chair back!
       [MOODY *enters on the private side. He sees* CHRIS *leaving and hears him shouting. From behind him* KEVIN *wheels on.* MOODY *turns and sees* KEVIN.]

MOODY: Here you! [KEVIN *spins round.*] Now I've got you, you little monkey! I've seen some cruel things in my lifetime but never anything quite as cruel as this!

KEVIN: What?

MOODY: 'What?' 'What?', he asks! You think I haven't got eyes in my head! What are these then?

KEVIN: Teeth?

MOODY: Eyes! Dear me! Now say sorry to the little — [*He turns.*] Where did he go anyway?

KEVIN: Who?

MOODY: That little spastic whose wheelchair you took.

KEVIN: What spastic?

MOODY: You know very well what little spastic I'm talking about!

KEVIN: I ain't never seen a spastic!

MOODY: [*sarcastic*] Ha ha ha! Now get out of that chair!

KEVIN: I can't.

MOODY: Ha ha ha! Out of it!
[*He grabs hold of the chair to tip* KEVIN *out.*]

KEVIN: I can't. I can't walk!

MOODY: Oh no? And you can't play football either, can you?

KEVIN: Not at the moment, no. I've had an accident.

MOODY: Got run over by a car, I suppose?

KEVIN: Yeah, that's right!

MOODY: Ha ha ha! So why was that little spastic screaming for his chair back?

KEVIN: Cos he wanted to be a wheel-person.

MOODY: [*taken aback*] A wheel-person?

KEVIN: Yeah! He was the only leg-person!
[*MOODY shakes his head in utter disbelief.*]

MOODY: Ha bloody ha ha, pull the other one, it's got bells on it! Out!
[*He grabs hold of the chair roughly.* KEVIN *hangs on.*]

KEVIN: Let go! Let go of me!
[*MR. WRIGHT enters in his wheelchair.*]

WRIGHT: Here, you! What do you think you're doing?

MOODY: [*shaking KEVIN's chair*] I'm trying to help a spastic!

WRIGHT: He's not a spastic!

MOODY: I didn't say he was, did I? This little ruffian has stolen a chair off a spastic. Now come on, out!

[*He grabs the chair again.* KEVIN *yells.*]

WRIGHT: Let him go, he can't walk!

[MOODY *releases* KEVIN.]

MOODY: But I've seen him walk!

[MOODY *walks over to* MR. WRIGHT. MR. WRIGHT *wheels through the fence.*]

WRIGHT: When? When did you see him walk?

[PAULA *comes on with* CHRIS's *wheelchair, behind* MOODY.]

MOODY: [*Steps back a couple of paces.*] Er . . . the other day.

WRIGHT: [*advancing on* MOODY] When? When?

MOODY: [*backing off*] Well, er . . . let me see . . . I don't know mm . . . I can't remember . . . [CHRIS *has now arrived and watches as* MOODY *backs unknowingly towards* PAULA's *wheelchair.*] . . . but I do know one thing!

WRIGHT: What?

MOODY: He shouldn't be in a wheelchair.

WRIGHT: Why not?

MOODY: Cos he can walk just as well as I can! Would *I* ever sit in a wheelchair? If I could walk instead!

[*He backs into* PAULA's *wheelchair and sits in it. She wheels him round the stage. He is shouting wildly. Finally he grabs her wrists.*]

PAULA: [*Stops.*] Ow!

MOODY: Now let me out!

MUM: [*Enters with shopping bags.*] Hey you! Do you mind! That's my daughter! [MOODY *lets go of* PAULA.] And that wheelchair you're sitting in belongs to my son!

[MOODY *steps out of the wheelchair but because he hasn't put the brakes on the chair goes flying backwards. He shoots forward, falling onto the ground with a yell.*]

MOODY: Ow! I think I've broken my leg!

CHRIS: Do you want to borrow my crutches?

[MUM *wheels* CHRIS's *chair over to him and he sits.*
MOODY *scrambles to his feet.*]

MUM: Now what's going on here?

WRIGHT: I think there's been a bit of a misunderstanding.

KEVIN: He thought I was sitting in Chris's wheelchair.

MUM: [*to* MOODY] On the contrary, you were sitting in Chris's wheelchair!

MOODY: How am I to know whose wheelchair is whose? Seems to me everyone's got a wheelchair these days! Just tell me one thing. [*He points to* KEVIN.] Can he walk or can't he?

ALL: No!

PAULA: He was in a car accident!

KEVIN: See!

MOODY: You mean he'll be like that . . . for life?

KEVIN: No. Only for about six weeks. If I'm lucky.

MOODY: Oh . . . er . . . [*He pats* KEVIN *on the shoulder.*] . . . sorry.

KEVIN: That's all right. Hey Mister! How about letting us play here then?

PAULA: Oh yeah, please Mister!

CHRIS: Please!

MOODY: Oh . . . er . . . all right then.

KIDS: Hooray!

MOODY: But er . . . that's our secret, eh?

CHRIS: And now you can guard this land for us!

KEVIN: Hey, yeah, Paula! We can come here after school, and play with Chris when he gets home.

MOODY: Don't you all go to the same school?

KEVIN: No, he can't go to our school.

MOODY: Why not?

KEVIN: Cos he's in a wheelchair.

MOODY: So are you.

KEVIN: The Headmistress knows about me, and she said I could.

CHRIS: In a wheelchair? In an ordinary school?

KEVIN: Yeah, I'm the first!

CHRIS: OK, then! I'll be the second! How about it, Mum?

MUM: That's all very well, Chris, but I'm afraid it can't be done.

CHRIS: Why not?

MUM: Christopher! With all the difficulties you've got . . .

WRIGHT: So he's got difficulties. The other children can always help him out.

CHRIS: And when they've got problems, I can help them!

WRIGHT: And that's why we're going down to that school tomorrow morning to talk to the Headmistress personally.

MUM: I don't know . . .

CHRIS: Oh go on, Mum!

MUM: Are you sure it can be done?

WRIGHT: Look, no-one says it's going to be easy. But let's give it a try, yeah?

Song: STRONGER THAN SUPERMAN

If anyone says it's useless,
It can't be done, it's hopeless,
They've only got themselves to blame.
It's time to take some action, time to make it plain
We can work, we can play, we can learn from each other,
We can love, we can laugh, there's so much to discover.

There's many many folk in wheelchairs,
Many other folk on crutches,
Many many more are deaf or dumb,
However, maybe not as much as . . .

Those of us who look quite funny,
Those of us who look quite sad,
But if you'd only get to know us
You'll find it ain't so bad.

So, come out of the shadows, get out in the sun,
If we all pull together we can get plenty done,
We don't need a hero to do what we can
Together we're stronger than Superman!

[*Repeat last four lines ad lib.*]

THE END

FOUR THEMES FOR FOLLOW-UP WORK

THEME ONE: "You're a person. You're not just handicapped."

These are the words spoken by Paula as she steps out of the wheelchair at the start of Act One, Scene One, but is it so easy for non-handicapped people to see the handicapped firstly as people and only secondarily as handicapped?

Act One, Scene One

a) What are our reactions to Chris at the very start of the play when we don't know that he is handicapped? What impressions do we have of his personality? (Pity?)

b) What are our reactions to Paula when she enters in the wheelchair?

c) Do our reactions to Paula and Chris as people change when we discover that Chris, and not Paula, is handicapped?

Act One, Scene Two

In this scene Chris and Paula play 'Doctors and Nurses'. Paula immediately categorises Chris as the patient: "You're in a wheelchair, so you're the patient." Handicapped people are seen as 'ill' and 'in need of help'.

But Chris is also prejudiced against Paula as a girl: "Only boys are doctors. You're the nurse." Here we must also note that Chris has in the first scene demonstrated his prejudice against old people. When he discovers that old people are to live nearby, he says: "They should be put somewhere else...They can't play or anything...Like football!"—although, of course, his own grandfather was an exception.

In this scene Chris gives the role of the Doctor to Superman. Chris says that doctors never explain anything to the patients, a theme which is repeated with Mr. Wright in the following scene. Is this true? Should doctors explain more to their patients, or is it simply too complicated to understand?

Act One, Scene Three

In this scene Mr. Wright comes collecting money for old people. He is the first person outside the family whom we meet. His reactions to Chris are perfectly normal and friendly. Why do you think this is so?

At the end of the scene, after he has heard of the family's individual and collective problems, Mr. Wright says:"There's more to helping people than collecting money", and invites Chris to go shopping with him. Why do you think Chris has never been in a Supermarket before? Is it because he's a boy, and boys don't go shopping?

The theme of categorisation is summed up in the song:*"You don't give me the chance"*. The point is not that we can all do *everything* well but that categorisation of people by sex, or strength, or age, or race, reduces their possibilities of discovering what they really can do.

A short exercise in categorisation: when we think of handicapped people, do we associate them with:

Strength	or	Weakness
Happiness	or	Sadness
Independence	or	Helplessness
Health	or	Sickness
Togetherness	or	Loneliness
Intelligence	or	Stupidity
Work	or	Unemployment
Activity	or	Passivity
Usefulness	or	Uselessness
Beauty	or	Ugliness
Contented	or	Discontented

Is collecting money the best way to help the handicapped, or old people? Or is it merely a way of relieving a bad conscience and proving that we are good citizens? Collecting money also encourages the handicapped person to continue to see himself or herself as dependent on non-handicapped people. What could be more effectively done to bring handicapped people into an active role in our society?

During the first three scenes in Act One we get to know quite a bit about Chris. Do we get used to his being handicapped? Do we ever forget he is handicapped? Do we start to see him more as a person?

If so...in

Act One, Scene Four

when Mr. Moody, the security man, arrives, what do we think of his attitude towards Chris? Why does he think like he does? Are his views and actions shared by many people? Or is he an exception? What is his influence on Kevin?

How does Kevin reveal his prejudices and his fears of handicapped people in the way he behaves 1) to Paula   2) to Chris? Why do you think he is frightened of Chris? Do you think you would feel awkward and frightened in the company of handicapped people? What is Kevin's biggest mistake in relating to Chris, and how do Paula and Chris demonstrate this? Try it with your friends!

At the end of the scene, when Mr. Moody has to speak directly to Chris, which of the two is the cleverer?

The behaviour of Mr. Moody is shown as stupid, awkward (both physically and psychologically), and blind. He fails to see Chris as a person.

Act Two, Scene One

Here we meet Mr. Barraclough, the head of the local Social Services Department—the bureaucrat. He is not only blind but deaf!

CHRIS: [*about* KEVIN *in the wheelchair*] He's not physically handicapped.

MR. B: No?

CHRIS: No! I am!

MR. B: That sort of joke is not in the least funny, young man!

Why cannot Mr. Barraclough believe Chris? What is his attitude to Kevin? "He's not cheeky like you. He's a little bit retiring...Shy. Like all handicapped." Is that true of Kevin generally, or only in this scene? Are handicapped people in general 'shy' and 'retiring'? If so, is this because:

          a) they are stupid.

          b) they are not used to contact with non-handicapped people.

          c) non-handicapped people relate to them in such a stupid, awkward and condescending manner that they don't get a chance to relate normally.

Act Two, Scene Two

The cinema manager's reactions to Chris...

"We must be phoned in advance...All we require is half an hour's notice...On condition that he leaves his wheelchair in the foyer...Fire regulations, nothing to do with me...as yet no places specially designated for the handicapped..."

Are his reactions, and his rules for handicapped people reasonable? How is Mr. Wright treated? What about money and the expense of adapting the cinema for the handicapped? Or is it better spent on new car parks? Handicapped people in the cinema might be offensive to other customers. Do you think, for example, that Mr. Moody would go to that cinema if he saw handicapped people there regularly? Have you ever seen handicapped people in your cinema? If not, why not?

KEVIN: It ain't surprising, if you make it so difficult!

Act Two, Scene Three

In the final scene we see Kevin, Chris and Mr. Wright in wheelchairs: all for different reasons. We may all at some time in our lives become handicapped. Ten per cent of the world's population is handicapped—400,000,000 people. In England, this amounts to at least five million, with 800,000 in London alone.

THEME TWO: Chris's main problems as a handicapped person

a) Physical and medical problems

    1) Legs
    2) Head
    3) Bladder
    4) Sores
    5) Lack of sensation.

The Association for Spina Bifida and Hydrocephalus (ASBAH), Tavistock House North, Tavistock Square, London WC1H 9HJ can provide further information in detail.

Here, explanations of spina bifida could lead into discussions on other sorts of handicap: spasticity, blindness, deafness, etc.

"I don't regard myself as handicapped. I've always been this way. Right from birth. For me, my condition is perfectly normal, because I've never known what it was like to walk. What makes me feel handicapped is the way people behave to me, and my everyday problems with travelling and buildings". Chris. A 16-year-old with spina bifida.

b) School and work problems

If Chris's main problems are not physical and medical, what are they? Should he be in a special school? Or is he right to think he could go to Kevin's school? What would be the main difficulties for Chris in your school: the people, or the building? (Desks, corridors, steps, stairways, width of doors, toilets, etc.)

What do you think Chris's work opportunities are after he leaves school?

c) Problems with the man-made environment

Chris couldn't get on a bus to go to the cinema, and when he got to the cinema, he wasn't allowed in because of the complicated rules for handicapped people.

Is it possible to adapt our transport so that handicapped people can travel just as easily as other passengers?

       1) in private cars
       2) in buses
       3) in the Underground
       4) in aeroplanes
       5) in trains

What about Chris's leisure time? Could he easily get into your local cinema?

In the final scene Chris talks about "Our deadly enemies...Leg people ...Cos they think we're stupid...Worse than that. Cos they build their world with something really criminal: that should be punished with death! Steps! And stairs! And kerb-stones!"

Could Chris shop easily in your local baker's, newspaper shop, or supermarket? Would he be able to serve himself from a wheelchair? Would he be able to get past the cash desk?

Could Chris get in and out of a public telephone?

Could he go to a football match, into a restaurant or hotel?

Could he play in your children's playground?

Why have we not built a world where handicapped people can get around without difficulty? Is it because:

    a) we never come into contact with them, so we forget their needs?

    b) their needs are met by special institutions such as special schools, homes and workplaces, so they don't need to use the outside world?

    c) it's simply too expensive to adapt the world for the benefit of handicapped people, who don't contribute much to the economy anyway. Should they simply be thankful for what we have already provided? One of the reasons Mr. Moody gives for not building a sports field is that there is more profit in building a car park. Children are also economically weak. "Ain't gonna get it from your pocket-money!" Does that mean we shouldn't do more for children?

Have we not simply created a vicious circle?

We hide handicapped people away in special institutions

so: we rarely come into contact with them

so: we forget their needs

so: we continue to build a world that is difficult for handicapped people

so: (to help them?) we build them special institutions

so: we rarely come into contact with them...**so**...**so**...**so**...

THEME THREE: The handicapped family

Song: *How How How* in Act One, Scene One. In this scene, who is the mother more worried about—Paula or Chris? Why do you think Paula stayed away from home so long? Was it just curiosity about the new neighbourhood?

In Act One, Scene Three, the children play a game: Julius Caesar and the Slave.

PAULA: I'm fed up of being your slave!

What problems do the brothers and sisters of handicapped people have?

What extra problems has Chris's mum? Time: Getting up, feeding, travelling, general care, hospital visits, more washing. Expense: special clothes and shoes, apparatus, wheelchairs, adapting the home, using taxis if they haven't got a car.

How can this family survive and stay together? *How How How?*

Is it through more social workers?

            miracles like Lourdes?

            better financial care from the government?

            wider community care?

Final song: If we all pull together we can get plenty done, etc.

THEME FOUR: Strength and weakness

Handicapped people are usually perceived as weak and unattractive. Is our society to be only for the strong (physical and economic), and the beautiful: or is it to be for everyone?

How much are we influenced by films, TV and advertisements to value the 'strong' and 'beautiful', and dislike the 'weak' and 'ugly'?

Have you ever seen an advertisement which uses a handicapped person? If so, what impression of the handicapped did it give you? Have you ever seen an advert with an ugly woman? Or a weak man? Are handicapped people weaker and more stupid than the rest of society? In the play everyone who sees themselves as individually stronger (either mentally or physically) is shown to be stupid: Mr. Moody, Kevin, Mr. Barraclough. As for the Cinema Manager, his use of physical force on Kevin leads to disaster.

Also published by Amber Lane Press

Dreams and Deconstructions:
Alternative Theatre in Britain

Edited by Sandy Craig

This illustrated account of the 'fringe' offers a critical
assessment of major writers and their plays, with chapters
on community and 'ethnic' theatre, political theatre,
children's theatre and theatre-in-education, performance art,
the regional reps and the workings of the Arts Council of
Great Britain.

192 pages   £7.95 (hardback)   £4.95 (paperback)

For further information on all
Amber Lane plays and theatre books,
send a stamped, addressed envelope to:

Amber Lane Press
9a Newbridge Road
Ambergate
Derbyshire DE5 2GR